KALEIDOSCOPE

EAST YORKSHIRE

Edited by Carl Golder

First published in Great Britain in 1999 by
POETRY NOW YOUNG WRITERS
Remus House,
Coltsfoot Drive
Woodston
Peterborough, PE2 9JX
Telephone (01733) 890066

HB ISBN 0 75430 437 X
SB ISBN 0 75430 438 8

FOREWORD

This year, the Poetry Now Young Writers' Kaleidoscope competition proudly presents the best poetic contributions from over 32,000 up-and-coming writers nationwide.

Successful in continuing our aim of promoting writing and creativity in children, each regional anthology displays the inventive and original writing talents of 11-18 year old poets. Imaginative, thoughtful, often humorous, *Kaleidoscope East Yorkshire* provides a captivating insight into the issues and opinions important to today's young generation.

The task of editing inevitably proved challenging, but was nevertheless enjoyable thanks to the quality of entries received. The thought, effort and hard work put into each poem impressed and inspired us all. We hope you are as pleased as we are with the final result and that you continue to enjoy *Kaleidoscope East Yorkshire* for years to come.

CONTENTS

Stephanie Dee	55
Ben Fisher	55
Kirsty Broom	56
Miriam Train	56
Jonathan Harper	57
Daniel Grantham	57
Robert Hunt	57
Philippa Cottrell	58
Keith Stephenson	59
Tara Murray	60
Ellie Hailwood	60
Andy Boothby	61
James Place	62
Stephen Norris	62
Matthew Blanchard	62
Steven Wood	63

Vermuyden School

Amanda Ritchie	63
David Locke	64
Sarah Hewson	65
John Johnson	65
Steven Hicks	66
Sean Lilley	67
Samantha Hobson	68
Lisa Shipley	68
Ruth Broughton	69
Simon Locke	69
Andrew Woolass	70
Poppy Bolton	70
Adam Price	71
Vikki Grant	72
Robert Hague	73
Hayley Chiswell	74
Michael Smith	74
Lucy Pollard	75
Adele Smithson	76
Jayne Storey	76

Ryan Gamewell	77
Paul Martin	78
Lynsey Charles	78
Charlotte Marston	79
Steven Collins	79
Samantha Hale	80
Stuart Stow	80
Nicola Sykes	81
Hannah Frances Bennett	81
Heidi Epton	82
Natalie Spavin	82
Liam Hoier	83
Kaley Munday	83
Sophie Howard	84
Lee Gelder	84
Emma Credland	85
Lisa Mapplebeck	86
Simon Standring	86
Emily Harding	87
Julie Stainton	88
William Chatham	88
Emma Blacker	89
Lee Barker	89
Kimberley Leckenby	90
Katie Hodgson	90
Laura Whiteley	91
Chris Pollard	91
Christopher Smithson	92
Shane Tavinder	92
Melanie Hodgson	93
Emma Raywood	93
Nicholas Hobson	94
Rebecca Hunter	94
Michael Hague	95
Amy Risebury	96
Anne Morris	96
Kirsty Stephenson	97
Gary Bray	98

The Poems

FIRE

A huge mass of anger and rage,
Anything it touches is crushed under the hate.
No good can be taken from it once it has escaped.
All goodness has drained away.
Its merciless path will not be destroyed, it trusts no one.
Leaving a path of destruction.
Burning the peaceful atmosphere of the earth.
Life will die if it tries to fight.
Never survive once the everlasting anger
Is aglow inside its heart.
All goodness has been smothered in
The early stages.
No more hope can be found.

Gemma Timperley (13)
Beverley High School

MY POEM

I'm a hyena who laughs a lot when running away from the enemy.
I'm a drink of Coca Cola with ice cubes in the glass.
I'm a jar of chocolate spread, thick and creamy over my bread.
I'm a daisy so pretty to see in the ground, getting watered and fed,
growing slender and tall each day.
I'm the thunder and lightning in the sky roaring loudly across
the clouds.
I'm a Ellesse jumper hanging on the clothes horse for someone
to pick up and I was in the sale for £5.99.
I'm a green blow-up settee - if a heavy person came and sat on me
I would *pop!*

Emma Shipley (11)
Beverley High School

ME!

I am a daisy, very small and innocent
being swept up in the breeze,
and a long slithery, scaly snake waiting to
pounce on you out of the reeds.
I am the snow, cold, wet and bright clear white.
I am a glass of cherryade that bubbles over the top
of the glass when you pour me.
I am a lovely citrus yellow shining out
onto the world,
and a slice of chocolate flake cake
dripping with sticky chocolate sauce.
I am a tiger striped inflatable chair
hanging up in a shop window, all lonely
and sad, hoping someone will buy me.
I'm a dazzling purple bobble hat showing
off my colour to the people that walk by.

Sophie Leach (11)
Beverley High School

A POEM OF ME

I'm a dazzling purple that sparkles up your eyes.
I'm a roaring tiger that leads a pack.
I'm a fizzy cherryade bottle waiting to go *pop!*
I'm a gorgeous caramel bar that wants to melt in your mouth.
I'm a little bluebell that's in your garden.
I'm a beautiful rainbow that's in the blue sky.
I'm a comfy chair that you won't want to get out of.
I'm some brand new trainers waiting to be worn.

Jade Mant (11)
Beverley High School

I AM A . . .

I'm a leopard ready to pounce on
anything that springs on me!
I'm a hurricane, crazy and wild
just like a small child.
I'm a long daunting black skirt,
wicked but smooth, with me you cannot
go wrong.

I'm bright orange and I fizz out
of control.
I'm a soft feathered bed, bouncy
and warm, soft for you to sleep
on until sunrise.
I am a round yellow daisy with
lots of pointed petals.
I will not give a fright in the night.
I'm soft and creamy, lush and brown,
yummy as can be, *'chocolate'*.

Rebecca Murray (11)
Beverley High School

MY POEM

I am a lime green leaf blowing in the wind.
I am a cheeky little monkey swinging from tree to tree.
I am a glass of coke ready to overflow.
I am a lovely yellow melon all juicy and wet.
I am a tall sunny sunflower shining in the sun.
I am a pair of wet trousers blowing on the line.
I am a blow-up settee with air blowing me up.

Rebecca Louise Harvey (11)
Beverley High School

SNOWY THE POLAR BEAR!

I'm a chubby white, cuddly polar bear,
plodding in the cold, wet snow.
My little paws are sore and red, and hurt as I go.
My bright lime green sweater
is keeping me cosy and warm.
It's very cold, you know it's blowing a storm.

I have an inflatable chair
inside my cosy cave.
It's very soft, you know, for my sensitive head.
It's softer than my warm bed.
I love eating Galaxy, it's very delicious and yummy.
If I eat too much I'll get a poorly tummy.
I like drinking Pepsi but it sometimes makes me burp.

Leanne Ashman (11)
Beverley High School

THE MYSTERIOUS LIFE OF ME!

I'm the secret scarlet of a cocktail dress.
I'm the chaise longue - elegant, attractive and royal.
I'm the sting on a nasty and vicious nettle,
always on my guard, with the wind rustling behind me.
I purr to those who I take kindly too,
but to those I suspect, I *raw* like a tiger!
I'm swirly and swooshy as I'm spaghetti bologne12se!
I'm Apple Hooch giving a fizz and a buzz to
everyone who sips and swigs!
I'm thunder and storm, people take fright and listen.
I'm the centre of attention!

Laura Tacey (11)
Beverley High School

ME!

I'm a friendly, freely jumping dolphin,
with my silver fin glistening in the sun.
I'm the tranquil aqua sea lapping on the golden sand.
I'm the multicoloured hula skirt of the exotic dancing girl.
And I'm the fizzing, bubbling, swirling Apple Tango
trying my best to escape my prison.
I am also the menacing hailstone with my giant marble-like balls
clattering on windows and crashing on doors.
I'm the rich dark chocolate that melts in your mouth.
I'm the blasting stereo with my deafening music.
I'm dying to be heard.
And I'm the sweet swaying forget-me-not
And I'll be in your memory forever more.

Holly Jo Clark (11)
Beverley High School

ME!

I'm blue and calm, I'm the middle of the ocean,
A dolphin jumping and dancing.
I'm bubbly cider fizzing up your nose,
A plate of lasagne, saucy and runny.
I'm a big sunflower lazing in the sun,
Wafting in the wind.
I'm a rainbow bright and colourful,
Or a pillow fluffy and soft.
I'm a pair of Nike Air Max,
I'm very expensive!

Sara Corlyon (11)
Beverley High School

ME!

I'm a horse galloping in the fields.
I'm a rose standing tall and straight
shooting to the sky.
I'm a bright blue blanket covering my body,
to keep me warm.
I'm an ice-cream sitting on a cone
in the comfort of my home.
I'm also a fizzy drink in a glass with lemons
on my side and popping out all over.
In the winter I am as white as snow,
I'm fluffy and soft and very cold.
I'm a big fluffy skirt blowing in the wind.
I'm a big pink stool standing by a chair.
I'm full of things that no one sees in the winter.

Emma Hutchinson (11)
Beverley High School

SARAH'S POEM

I'm a nice little, cute, naughty monkey.
I am a pink fluffy dress smothered in fur.
I'm a nice cosy bed waiting for someone to get in me,
but beware, I can be like thunder and lightning
roaring through the night.
I'm a red rose in your hand, I wait.
I am chocolate whip waiting for someone to dig
a spoon into me.
I am cool and fizzy Tango! *Drink me!*
I am the colour red, that means *love!*

Sarah Louise Townsend (11)
Beverley High School

MYSELF

I am a tall square mirror
with a corner to every side
of me.
A fast escaping tiger
running away from
"   trouble.
I am a bright yellow colour
shining like the sun.
I am 9 pm at night, fast asleep
in bed.
I am a sweet smelling rose
sunbathing in the garden.
A foggy, frosty morning
when I first get out of bed.
I am a fluffy fur coat
protected from cold
weather.
I'm lemonade, popping
and fizzing in a jar.

Annie Richards (12)
Beverley High School

BONFIRE NIGHT

Bonfire night, sparklers waving
Look! The fire is burning.
It's bonfire night, the rockets go
up and up, the Catherine wheels
are whirring.
The colours burst before your eyes
It's bonfire night!
Guy Fawkes is burning.

Esther Smith (11)
Beverley High School

PEOPLE POEM

I am a window to see two sides of.
I am a lion to be afraid of.
I am a bright sharp vicious *red.*
I am 11 pm because everything's still.
I am a rose, sharp but beautiful.
I am a cloud to enjoy the sun
when I want and to block it out
when I don't.
I am a skirt that can wave and
move freely.
I am a cup of shiny, cool, crisp
apple juice.
And I am proud to be all
of *these!*

Samantha Hodgson (11)
Beverley High School

ABOUT ME!

I'm a sticky toffee pudding, gooey and nice.
I'm a blue silky, sparkling nightdress
lying in bed with my dreams.
I'm fizzy apple juice popping all over,
making me dizzy.
I'm a sofa sitting outside taking it easy.
I'm snow coming down white from the sky.
I'm a pink rose sparkling all night, standing in a pose.

Sophie Weatherill (11)
Beverley High School

People Poem

I am a bull in a china shop.
A long skirt, all black and dull.
I am a pink, bright lily because
I shine in the light.
I also can be a thunderstorm
when I want to be.
I am also a rocking horse
because
I rock with excitement.
I am a 12.00 o'clock girl,
not too late, not too early.
I am a bottle of fizzing coke all
bubbly and always going pop.
I am the colour red,
all hot and spicy.

Emma Kirby (12)
Beverley High School

Me!

I'm a horse that is standing in the sun
and I get ridden all the time.
I'm the man who is green from Mars.
I'm the person who drinks all the milk,
my skin is creamy and soft.
I'm the Mars bar who gets eaten by everybody
and I do not like it.
I'm the red rose that has grown from a seed.
I'm the person who likes to wear shorts
in hot weather.

Hannah Stanton (11)
Beverley High School

MYSELF

I am a soft sofa, new from the shop.
I am a puppy bouncing, always active.
I am a bright and colourful orange,
always standing out.
I am always 7 o'clock at night,
a time to relax.
I am a rose bud in spring,
just about to blossom into a pink rose.
I am blue sky, not too cold and
not too warm.
I am a pair of long tight trousers
that are black and made of cotton.
I am a cool and clear glass of water
that makes the nearest mouth water.

Caroline Upton (11)
Beverley High School

A POEM ABOUT ME

I'm a mouth-watering fudge cake,
with pouring chocolate sauce.
A tiny fox cub scrambling to get out the den,
only just being able to see.
I'm the colour of yellow, with a hint of black.
The fizzy, tangy colour of limeade trying to spurt out.
I'm the bright sun shining down making your eyes squint.
A pair of torn blue jeans getting worn out.
A big sunflower towering high above, almost reaching the sky.
I'm a desk standing lonely and quietly in the corner of a room.

Sarah Burnett (11)
Beverley High School

WORLD

Bombing,
Bombing.
After all the bombing.
After all the bombing you would
have thought,
You would have thought that the
world would have gone.

Gone,
Gone.
The world seems so empty,
It seems what the world would
be like.

Empty,
Empty.
Empty is what our hearts are like
with nobody to love.

Sophia Burns (12)
Beverley High School

DANIELLE!

I am a storm - wild, mysterious and wonderful.
I am a long red silk dress making people look.
I am a tiger on the trail of something smelling sweet.
I am the colour red - deep, rich and romantic.
I am cream leather - cuddly, soft and luxurious.
I am a pint of beer waiting for someone.
I am a chocolate fudge cake - soft, creamy and tasty.
I am a red rose spreading my petals on a fine summer morning.

Danielle Kearney (11)
Beverley High School

CHRISTMAS

Father Christmas is eating pie
His reindeer are getting ready to fly
First they have their morning snack
While Father Christmas packs his toy sack
Tom and Jess leave the reindeer carrots
And we all know reindeer love carrots.

Outside the leaves are brown and crispy
Spiders' webs are white and wispy
Snow laid flat upon the grass
My favourite season has come at last
I wish my friends would come and play
I hope the snow will last all day.

Kids in Germany are buying shoes
Father Christmas has to choose
Who's been good and who's been bad
So all be good or you'll end up sad.

Merry Christmas!

Laura Menzies (12)
Beverley High School

ELLA

I am a pony galloping through the woods,
I am fresh pure orange juice waiting to be poured,
I am a short skirt showing my legs!
I am a bouncy, springy bed! *Bounce, bounce!*
I am a hot bright sun shining in the sky,
I am a bright red poppy that'll catch your eye,
I am mint chocolate ice-cream cooling in the fridge,
I am a glistening gold wax crayon sparkling in my box.

Ella Barton (11)
Beverley High School

COME TO THE ZOO

Come to the zoo, it's only £1.03,
Men, women and children come totally free!
See the chimps swing and eat their food,
Stay right away, they can be quite rude!
Take leave of work and have a rest,
Then come to this crazy zoo, it's the best!

It's highly hygienic, and very secure
Where the animals come to drop their manure.
Visit the snakes, to experience their sting,
Sorry, don't! What a horrible thing.

Near the end of the day, see the hippos swim,
Don't get too close you could break your limb!
If you're hungry meet the gorillas, they'll treat you like a queen,
Try the bananas, and eat coconut cream,
You will really believe you're in a dream.

Charmaine Ilangaratne (11)
Beverley High School

THE GOOD AND BAD SIDE OF ME

I am a smelly sock, getting horrible and sweaty.
I am fog, thick and mean.
I am weak weed.
I am a hyena, I laugh at things I shouldn't.
I am yellow bright as the sun.
I am champagne, ready for the party.
I am a Yorkshire pudding plump and fluffy.
I am a sofa comfy and cosy,
Come and squash me!

Jennifer Marin (11)
Beverley High School

DAYDREAMING

When I daydream
I can be a queen,
A knight in shining armour,
And now I'm good at drama
I'm a swimmer and a gymnast
A Concorde aeroplane
An elephant and crow
I am free wherever I go.

When I daydream
I have seen
Aliens all blue and green
Brightly coloured monsters
Make me shout and scream
I fly so high
Like a bird in the sky
But you can't catch me
Neither can I.

Joanne Jones (11)
Beverley High School

ME!

I am the lovely colour navy,
I am a soft and squeaky guinea pig,
I am a bottle of champagne, *pop popping,*
I am a lovely soft piece of fudge,
I am a lovely flower called Bizzy Lizzy,
I am a hot and sweaty sun,
I am a striped tie,
And I am a hi-fi system which makes such a noise.

Elizabeth Ruth Fenwick (11)
Beverley High School

WAR

I feel lost,
Trapped from the world outside
Worried about the future
Distressed, unwanted and angry
Questions are buzzing in my mind

Where will I go? What will happen to me?
I am upset
I envy those who will be staying behind
I feel weak, ill and upset
I am *petrified!*

Worry, sadness, weakness and unhappiness
These are a few things running through my mind
Questions ringing in my head
Hate, for the people who have started this mess
Anxiousness at the thought of the person who will take me!
Will anyone take me? I feel ill at the thought!
Help!

Gabrielle Meade (11)
Beverley High School

WHAT I WOULD BE

I am a very cold bottle of fizzy champagne, I make you drunk!
I am the tuna that makes the sandwich.
I am the red rose that shows you I love you.
I am a roaring hot sun.
I am a beautiful scarf that snuggles around your neck.
I am a graceful unicorn dancing in the sky.
I am a soft sofa, sit on me and you won't want to get off me.

Catherine A Milner (11)
Beverley High School

KALIHA

To some people this may not make sense,
it does to me,
it's my magic word,
when I'm in trouble I shout *'Kaliha'*,
it makes the person forget,
instead they give me a lolly or a bag of
sweets.
Or if my friend and me are arguing
I shout it as loud as I can,
they forget all about it and start to
wonder why their face is all red and
why their fists are clenched so tight,
it also makes me feel happy that it's
my magic word and no one else's.

Lucy Buckley (11)
Beverley High School

ME!

I'm a huge, bright, dazzling daffodil.
I am a jumpy kangaroo, bouncing everywhere.
I'm a comfy, squashy chair waiting to be sat on.
I'm a big black rain cloud producing floods
everywhere I go.
I'm a bright shiny, happy yellow.
I'm a fizzy drink of Tango with orange bubbles popping.
I'm a long piece of spaghetti, thin and stringy.
I'm a big and black clompy boot.

Rachael Bayliss (11)
Beverley High School

I'M A ...

I'm a tomato to eat.
I'm a tiger waiting to pounce.
I'm a darling daffodil dreaming of spring.
I'm a tracksuit running down the street.
I'm the rain wetting anything in my way.
I'm the orange in an orange.
I'm a soft and cosy sofa, so come sit on me.
I'm lemon juice about to be drunk.

Georgina Freelance (11)
Beverley High School

PEOPLE POEMS

I am bright and fiery, wild red
I am a pair of sparkly hipsters shining at night
I am a hedgehog, a deep, deep fog
I am a mug of boiling hot chocolate,
flowing over the sides
I am comfortable sofa bed at 9.00 pm.

Stephanie Reid (11)
Beverley High School

PEOPLE POEM

I am soft, sandy and warm.
I am soft and squashy.
I am a baby foal enjoying the soft gentle sun.
Ding dong, 6 o'clock, a time to relax.
I am a soft, gentle, warm horse rug.
I am a glass of hot chocolate waiting
beside the kettle getting cold.

Donna Whittle (11)
Beverley High School

The Kingdom Of Birds

The green expanse stretches
before me I walk on and enter.
A captivating scene awaits me.
The thrush and skylark
dance together.
The robin and his mate.
For the eagle has landed,
the king is here.

The blue tit and
the swallow dance
lightly on the wind,
a beautiful display
performed for my eyes.
For the eagle has landed,
the king is here.

A sudden twittering
begins, the owl and
peacock spread their
wings, and fly high
over the green expanse.
For the eagle has landed,
the king is here.

His mate alights
upon the branch.
He turns to face her
and they dance upon
a breath of air.
They fly away

The others scatter
and I am left to
watch in wonderment,
and the green expanse
closes upon me.
I am alone,
in the kingdom of birds.

Zophia Clegg (12)
Beverley High School

PEOPLE POEM

I'm the warming sun on a cold day,
I'm a holly bush at Christmas time,
I'm a fizzing, bubbling can of coke,
I'm a comfy TV chair,
I'm a man eating shark, looking for flesh,
I'm a pair of stylish knee high boots,
I'm always 8.32 pm, just in time for supper,
I'm yellow and bright and sunny.

Amy Robertson (12)
Beverley High School

PEOPLE POEM

She's bright retro-pink with yellow dots
A big, comfy armchair
A bouncy, energetic Labrador
And a 10 am (sleep inner)
She's a gentle rose
But a fiery thunderstorm
A split mini skirt
And a drink of cola full of fizz!

Julia Jennings (12)
Beverley High School

My Dog Buster

Buster likes going walkies.
He loves walking all the time.
So when we take him out each night
We sing a little rhyme.

Walkies Bust, walkies Bust,
Walkies, walkies, walkies Bust.

Buster likes his titbits.
He's always begging for more.
If we have a biscuit.
He always gives his paw.

Biscuits Bust, biscuits Bust,
Biscuits, biscuits, biscuits Bust.

Buster likes to wrestle,
He likes to pounce and fight,
But if we get too rough with him,
He starts to bark and bite.

Barking Bust, biting Bust.
Barking, biting, barking Bust.

Buster hates the vacuum cleaner,
He hides behind the chair,
Will he come out to play again?
No chance, he wouldn't dare!

Scary Bust, scary Bust.
Scary, scary, scary Bust

Buster is going wee-wees now,
Because it's time to go to bed.
But will he obey - do as he's told
You bet, because my dad said!

Wee-wees Bust, wee-wees Bust,
Wee-wees, wee-wees,
Wee-wees Bust.

Jennifer Holborn (11)
Beverley High School

PEOPLE POEM

I am a bright orange like a burning fire
I am a soft, squashy cushion
I am a horse galloping in the wind
I am 3.00 pm, ready and rearing to go
I am a pansy big, bright and beautiful
I am the sun shining happiness everywhere
I am a skirt swishy, swaying everywhere
I am a drink of hot chocolate nice, lovely and warm.

Rachel Warrington (11)
Beverley High School

PEOPLE POEM

I am orange, a warm colour when it's cold,
I am an evening on a warm summer's night,
I am a little fluffy rabbit bouncing around,
I am a big radio because I always talk,
I am a lightning bolt because I suddenly come,
I am a can of lemonade, a rather fizzy drink,
I am a daisy as sweet as can be (sometimes)!

Hannah Robinson (11)
Beverley High School

PEOPLE POEM

I am a door, hard and sturdy.
I am a fox, cautious, soft and gentle.
I am the yellow of the warm sun
and the blue of the sea.
I am 9 pm, I enjoy my sleep
like a hamster.
I'm a Venus fly trap, always hungry
and can be very snappy and vicious.
I'm a storm, fierce and can get very angry
if I get annoyed.
I'm a pair of old boots, well worn.
I'm water, plain and clear.

Gillian Cawood (11)
Beverley High School

PEOPLE POEM

I am a navy blue colour mysterious,
I am a stool for little children to sit on,
I am a giraffe, tall and quiet,
I am seven pm, a still time,
I am a poppy sometimes restless
but sometimes calm,
I am a warm and windy autumn,
I am a long flowing skirt,
I am a glass of cool apple juice
sitting in the sun.

Olivia Booth (11)
Beverley High School

EVERMORE

I was sitting on my own
Wondering, thinking
All alone.
I was sitting in the corner
Freezing, sneezing
I was cold, I wasn't moving
I was slowly, slowly falling
Slowly sleeping
Sleep no more.
I was lying on the floor
Dying, dying
Evermore
Evermore
Evermore

Helen Cockerton (11)
Beverley High School

PEOPLE POEM

She is the colour yellow all day
She is a bouncy, springy bed
She is a cuddly white rabbit, all fluffy and soft
She is a ten o'clock in the morning
(because that's when she gets up!)
She is a perfect little tulip, all rosy and shy
She is a bright, cloudless, sunny day
She is a halter-neck top from Miss Selfridge.
She is a fizzy can of Diet Coke
Waiting to be opened in a burst of fizz.

Colette Atkinson (12)
Beverley High School

PEOPLE POEM

I am a starfish,
Swimming and being the star of the sea,
Then at night I become a star twinkling and sparkling with my love star,
Or sometimes in the day I am a coffee table opposite a warm big
                                                                    red fire,
But in the summer a pure glass of orange, homemade,
Maybe a soft, sweet slow flowing river by the countryside.

Philippa Kirby (11)
Beverley High School

PEOPLE POEMS

I am a fizzy drink, sharp and tangy.
I'm orange, lovely and warm.
I am a gerbil scurrying around.
A television is what I am, always talking and dramatic.
I'm a lily floating on the calm pond.
I am a snowflake falling gently from the sky.
I'm a woolly jumper, soft and warm.

Lyndsey Maynard (11)
Beverley High School

PEOPLE POEMS

I am a bright orange and lively.
I am a highchair for babies to sit in.
I am a calm but humorous elephant.
I am 3.50 pm, home time!
I am warm and breezy.
I am a pair of shorts on a warm day.
I am an ice cold glass of forest fruits.

Emma Clark (11)
Beverley High School

PEOPLE POEMS

I am floaty dreamy blue,
Like a snowdrop
Waving in a light breeze.
I am a carefree dolphin
Gliding through the calm blue ocean.
I am a dainty blue skirt *
Swaying as the wind catches me.
I am fizzy lemonade,
Popping away under the warm sun.
I am a comfy, soft sofa
Lazily resting all day long.
I am seven o'clock,
Waiting and ready for action.

Amy Mercer (12)
Beverley High School

PEOPLE POEM

I am a bright orange colour.
I am a comfy armchair.
I am a spotted leopard leaping
through the jungle.
I am 3.50 on a Friday afternoon.
I am a yellow daffodil moving
with the wind.
I am a hot, bright summer's day.
I am a warm pair of gloves.
I am a bottle of lemonade which
fizzes up like my laughter.

Lucy Clark (11)
Beverley High School

THROUGH THE WINDOW

Through the window,
Flowers are blooming,
Birds are singing,
Grass is green.

Through the window,
The sun has arrived,
Hot and sticky,
Hayfever starting.

Through the window,
There is an autumn tree,
Leaves all gone,
Cold and bare.

Through the window,
Winter has come,
A white sheet of snow,
Covering the ground.

Hannah Fitzpatrick (12)
Beverley High School

PEOPLE POEMS

I am turquoise like the sea rushing from shore to shore.
I am a soft cushion for people to rest on.
I am an active tiger living in a dangerous jungle.
I am 8 pm, a time for relaxing.
I am a snowdrop that comes in the winter.
I am the snow that brings the winter.
I am a comfortable jumper to keep people warm.
I am a warm drink of hot chocolate.

Charlotte Walker (11)
Beverley High School

A Pupil's Worst Nightmare!

Slam, bang,
I'm in from school,
I can't believe my teacher's a fool.
If only she would listen to me,
Maybe she will let me be.
If she rings my mum tonight,
I'll tell you now I'll be dead before light.
I forgot to hand my homework in,
She is acting as if it was a terrible sin.
I tried to explain, I really did,
But she replied 'Don't go there kid!'
It ended up being a dream,
As I started to yell and scream.

Helen Jessop (13)
Beverley High School

People Poems

I am a wardrobe because I like my clothes.
I am a curious cat.
I am a slow flowing misty blue.
My time of day is 10.30 because I am always up.
I am a sunflower because I like my sun.
I am a long breeze as I think before I do things.
I am a purple velvet dress because I'm sly and sleek.
I am a fizzy cream soda.

Laura Chapman (11)
Beverley High School

SOAP

A bar of soap is a funny old thing
It starts off thick and then goes thin
Like our friend, the gingerbread man, he
shouts 'You'll never catch me!'
Dipping and diving, desperate to be free
Around the bath he slips and slides
If you're not careful he'll jump over the side.
At last, you think you've gone and won.
Your silly old mum goes and buys another one.
So the chase begins all over again
Oh chasing a bar of soap is such a pain!

Rachael Lambert (11)
Beverley High School

PEOPLE POEMS

I am light blue like the blue sky.
I am a bouncy cushion.
I am a galloping horse which leaps
over poles and bridges.
I am a clock at 6.30 all the time.
I am a sunflower that glows in the sun.
I am the gleaming, glittering white snow
that falls from the freezing sky.
I am a pair of baggy trousers.
I am a bottle of cola, that is very fizzy.

Rachel Sampson (12)
Beverley High School

AS THE WATER FALLS

A crying, splashing waterfall
rushing and flowing
down the river Doe.
The water was
roaring like a lion.
Like a curtain
it watched it
twisting, twirling,
swirling, whirling
and weaving round the rocks
until it became calm
returning to its normal speed.

Olivia Coates (12)
Beverley High School

MYSELF

I am a small inquisitive bookshelf,
A pounding kitten who's never settled.
My colour is lilac.
I am 6 am, the rising sun.
I am a field of daisies.
I am white fluffy snow.
I am a long silky dress.
And I'm a soft fruity Calypso drink,
That's me!

Hannah White (11)
Beverley High School

PEOPLE POEM

I'm a big, soft armchair
And sometimes I feel like a
bouncy, happy Labrador
I'm a cool ice blue colour
I feel like a midday breeze
I would like to be a lily
floating down a stream
I'm the hot, sweet sun, golden
I feel like a baby blue top
I'm a colourful cocktail in
a thin tall glass.

Cassie Page (11)
Beverley High School

PEOPLE POEMS

She is a bright orange, happy person.
She is a colourful, comfy sofa.
She is a wild horse riding free.
She is a night-time party girl.
She is a tall rose swaying in the wind.
She is a sunny summer's day.
She is a short, cool white dress.
She is a thirst quenching orange drink.

Emma Harle (11)
Beverley High School

PEOPLE POEM

I am a pencil-pot short and stout
I am a snowball hurling through the air
I am a teddy bear keeping my eye on you
I am a horse galloping through fields
I am a dustbin full of litter
I am a trophy showing off in the cabinet
I am a cup full of orange juice
I am a sack waiting to be worn
I am a photo frame with a picture in me
I am a girl laying thinking.

Lucy Rozenbroek (11)
Beverley High School

PEOPLE POEMS

I am yellow like the sun
and I am a soft comfy bed.
I am a small adventurous kitten.
I am the sun rise.
I am a smooth breeze on a summer's day.
I am a long thin dress.
I am a small thin sunflower.
I am a glass of sparkling lemonade.

Hannah Bayes (11)
Beverley High School

AT NIGHT

At night when the foxes are out lurking about
looking for prey, owls hooting in the trees,
searching for food.
Badgers looking for something to eat,
bats screeching everywhere in the sky,
hedgehogs scurrying about the cold frosty ground
with their spikes up in the air.
Tigers hiding in the bushes waiting to pounce
on some prey.
Dawn has broken and all nocturnal animals
fall fast asleep.

Kelly Waslin (11)
Beverley High School

PEOPLE POEM

She is a bright, yellow person
She is a bright light
She is a jumping rabbit
hopping through woods
She is a night person
She is a bright orange flower
in the sunlight
She is sunny weather
She is lemonade fizzing away.

Sophie Cressey (11)
Beverley High School

MY CAT

Soft, silky
Smooth, sleek
Clawing, pawing
Leaping, jumping
Darting, creeping
Pouncing, crawling
Licking, washing
Stalking, prowling
Fearless, fearful
Purring, miaowing
Spitting, hissing,
I love my cat.

Amy Brown (11)
Beverley High School

PEOPLE POEMS

She is multicoloured
A fluffy rug by the fire
A sleek cat with green eyes
A midnight walker
She is a welcoming daffodil
A bright sunshine on a summer's day
She is a pair of flares
A glass of summer fruit juice
A pot of noodles.

Laura Jack (11)
Beverley High School

PEOPLE POEM

I am a fizzy drink, bouncy and bubbly.
Also I'm the colour yellow, bright and warm.
I am a hamster, cute and sweet.
I'm a rose pretty with the occasional bad point.
I am a fluffy cloud floating in the blue sky.
A feather floating to the floor is what I am.
I'm a dress, flowered and flowy.
I'm a star, gold and twinkling in the midnight sky.
I am *me!*

Emily Harper (11)
Beverley High School

PEOPLE POEM

I am a light blue sky
I am a warm cosy chair
I am a soft playful kitten
I am 12.00 at midday
I am a beautiful daisy
I am a warm day
I am a warm soft jumper
I am cold apple juice.

Gemma O'Neill (11)
Beverley High School

PEOPLE POEMS

She is lime green full of colour
She's a peace lily in summer.
She's a fizzy drink full of energy
She's a pair of jeans.
Or a big ripe strawberry.
She's a sunny day   *
Or a big bouncy bed.
She's a 4:00pm person.
She's a small fish
Full of fun.

Sophie Bennett (11)
Beverley High School

PEOPLE POEMS

I am red in the morning
I am a brown armchair
I am a cat in the moonlight
I am ten to four on a Wednesday
I am a red rose
I am a breeze in the summer
I am a pair of flares on a winter's day
I am lemonade on a summer's day.

Charlotte Cox (11)
Beverley High School

PEOPLE POEMS

I'm orange because it's bubbly and bright,
I'm an inflatable sofa, if burst I take flight,
I'm a fat, lazy cat so I don't have to run,
I'm 5.00 teatime, now that's more like fun,
I'm a beautiful rose who's a prickly bush,
I'm a T-shirt for people getting dressed in a rush,
I'm a beer at the side of the family pool,
As for weather, I'm cloudy keeping everyone cool.

Laura Mitcheson (11)
Beverley High School

PEOPLE POEM

I'm a piece of furniture slouching about all day.
I'm a whining cat prowling about the streets.
I'm the sparkly colour blue dancing in the rain.
I'm a purple sunset setting in the sky.
I'm a daisy dancing in the sun.
I'm a strong breeze blowing the leaves off the ground.
I'm a woolly jumper cuddling a small girl.
I'm lemonade sparkling in the sun.

Lauren Middleton (11)
Beverley High School

PEOPLE POEMS

I'm a warm and cosy bed.
I'm a roaring lion when I'm angry.
I'm a bright coloured blue.
I'm the time midnight when I'm dreaming.
I'm a bright red coloured tulip.
I am the cold, cold snow in winter.
I'm a pair of black high wobbly heels.
I am a can of cool fizzy coke.

Louise Haigh-Walsworth (12)
Beverley High School

MYSELF

I am a television because I'm bright and bubbly,
I am a Springer Spaniel who can play about but can also fall asleep.
I am a light yellow because it's like sand on a tropical island,
I am 12.00 because it's the middle of the day,
I am a daisy because I'm always happy,
I am a sunny day cheering everybody up,
I am a short skirt because I like parties,
I am a cold drink of tropical flavoured water.

Emma Mann (11)
Beverley High School

PEOPLE POEM

I am a sofa all snugly and soft
I am a cat always running about
I'm the colour pink, so I am warm
I'm 12.00 so not too early or late
I'm a bright red rose always looking pretty
I am snow just drifting through the air
I'm a nice long denim skirt, so I'm dull
I'm a fresh orange juice, nice and healthy.

Rebecca Howard (11)
Beverley High School

MYSELF

I'm a strong, stiff table,
I'm a prowling squirrel,
I'm the shining, sparkling gold,
I like 12 o'clock especially when I'm hungry,
I'm the standing high rose,
I'm a big, fluffy bobble,
The golden sunshine shining down,
I'm the fizz that's in the fizzy orange.

Amy Wenn (12)
Beverley High School

MY PEOPLE POEM

I am a tall, dark wardrobe sitting in my room.
I am a bounding puppy running round and round.
I am a dark brown colour coming back from play.
I am 12.00 noon waiting for my lunch.
I am a lily floating gently in the water.
I am the sunshine, bright and happy.
I am a cotton jumper needing to get warm.
I am a bottle of bubbly champagne.
I am a juicy apple, crispy and green!

Samantha Wright (11)
Beverley High School

MYSELF

I'm a picture in a frame, hanging quietly.
I'm a swan on a lake swimming gracefully.
I can be light purple, light green, I'm mostly aquamarine.
My time is 6.00 am when the sun rises at dawn.
I'm a water lily jumping up and down on the bubbly stream.
I'm a calm wind but sometimes I'm a strong breeze.
I'm a tropical fruit juice, sunny and healthy.
I'm a pair of dungarees.

Charlotte Lancaster (11)
Beverley High School

MYSELF

I'm a big bookshelf full of information.
I'm a friendly Great Dane
because I'm full of energy.
I'm a cool icy blue.
I'm a bright sunflower, swaying in the breeze.
I'm a warm sunny day.
I'm a short purple top.
I'm fizzy and tropical like 'Lilt'.
I'm a free theme park
full of big rides.

Helen Lochead (11)
Beverley High School

PEOPLE POEM

I am a filing cabinet, organised and neat
I am a wild stallion galloping in the street
My colour is yellow
I am the night with shining stars, so bright
I am a daffodil, happy and smiley
I am calm but sometimes stormy
I am a jumper, warm and cuddly
My drink is champagne, light and bubbly.

Lucia Linfoot (11)
Beverley High School

PEOPLE POEMS

I am a big brown desk with lots of drawers
I am a tiny, hoppy, bright green frog
with big wide eyes
I am as blue as the sky
I am a lunchtime person
I am a bright, colourful yellow daffodil
I am a dazzling, fiery sun up in the sky
I am a pair of bright blue jeans
I am a tiny tin of coke brown and fizzy.

Sara Fawcett (11)
Beverley High School

MYSELF

I am a CD player that sits in the lounge.
I am a cat that is cuddly and soft.
I am a cool midsummer's blue sea.
I am the morning that is there every day.
I am a daffodil that comes every spring.
I am the sun, the head of warm weather.
I am a black pair of shoes that go disco dancing.
I am a glass of coca cola sparkling in the sun.

Amanda Hall (11)
Beverley High School

PEOPLE POEMS

I am a comfy chair in a warm room.
I am a fast cheetah in the long grass.
I am a bright yellow colour like the sun.
I am a fluffy cloud in the sky.
I am half a day at 12 o'clock.
I am different coloured tulips swaying in the breeze.
I am a jumper keeping someone warm.
I am a tropical drink with a straw in.
I am a bar of dark chocolate.

Anne Simpson (12)
Beverley High School

PEOPLE POEM

I am a bin to put your rubbish in,
or a radio, I make a din.
A bird to fly high in the sky,
a lovely round juicy, pink pork pie.
Soft, fluffy snow floating to the ground,
a warm woolly hat that I've just found.
A cup of hot chocolate that doesn't get cold,
red is the colour bright and bold.

Stephanie Hines (11)
Beverley High School

MYSELF

I'm a push button armchair,
I'm a jumpy, bumpy spider monkey,
I'm a light orange sunset setting in the sky,
I'm 8 o'clock in the lounge,
I'm a white lily standing in the sun,
I'm the frosted ice of winter,
I'm a pair of long hippy hipsters,
I'm a fruity, juicy cocktail.

Kayleigh Martin (11)
Beverley High School

ME!

I'm a melted strawberry ice-cream
I'm a blue silky dress
I'm a banana milkshake
I'm a tiny teddy bear laying in a sofa bed
I'm a little bunny rabbit sniffing
A white rose in the pouring rain.

Charlotte Turner (11)
Beverley High School

CATS

Cats everywhere on the wall or up a tree,
Lazing in front of the fire or laying on your favourite chair
Tripping you up or wandering about
Drinking milk and eating fish
What more could they ask for
Going missing and turning up
Sleeping on a rug.

Chérie Bryant (11)
Beverley High School

GUESS WHO?

I am light, white, bright, no doubt.
I am from pillows, birds I mustn't say the words.
Guess who I am?
Feather

I fly into space
I go faster than running in a race
I have fire coming out
I carry people about
I can go to the moon
You will get there very soon
What am I?
Rocket

I am high in the sky
I cannot fly
I shine very bright
I am very light
What am I?
Sun

I slither and slide along the ground
I am long but not round
I have a tongue and I can bite
I am sure to give you a fright
What am I?
Snake

I am grey
I have a trunk
I am not a small as a skunk
I am big, fat and
quite round
What am I?
Elephant.

Laura Gillard (11)
Beverley High School

MY STAY AT THE LODGE

I woke up early and crept out of the lodge

The door creaked but I got out undetected.

Slowly, I walked down the mossy path,
which led to the garden.

I walked into the greenhouse;

The fragrance of flowers raced up my nose
in a frenzy.

My eyes caught a glimpse of the
turquoise blue sky,

It glistens like a lake on a summer's day.

I sat for hours inhaling the sweet smell of buddleia.

Gradually, the sky turned jet black;

I headed back to the lodge,

I walked down the windy path,

I felt like someone was watching every move I made.

Twigs snapped brutally under my feet.

Rats scurried beneath the debris of fallen trees.

The wind wailed like a soul lost at sea!

I saw a glimpse of the porch light and
hurried on.

As I opened the door, the warmth of
the fire greeted my presence.

Charles Ryan (12)
Cottingham High School

THE KALEIDOSCOPE

It's very hot,
It's pretty,
It's very nice.
There's different colours and a picture of
Mickey Mouse.
Shake it,
Rattle.
Winding it, the pictures go;
Red, orange, green, yellow, blue, purple.
All the colours are going inside outside, orange,
Yellow, pink, green.
All different shapes.

Amy Roberts (12)
St Anne's County Special School, Welton

CHANGING COLOURS

Blue and yellow,
Red and green,
Making a shape.

Red,
Blue and red,
Changing colours to yellow and green.

Andrew Oliver (14)
St Anne's County Special School, Welton

RIVER

Colours are different,
Colours are moving quickly and fast,
Turning kaleidoscope,
And colours change.
Blue, green, yellow, orange, red, making pink purple.

Daniel Straight (15)
St Anne's County Special School, Welton

SISTER TO SISTER

When I see you smile,
I know you have achieved,
The world is cruel to you,
Yet you are as happy as can be.

When I see you cry,
I feel so guilty,
We take life for granted,
You face each challenge as it
Comes

When I see you,
One more tiny chromosome,
Is so bitter,
But you are so sweet.

Tracey I'Anson (13)
Withernsea High School

CHRISTMAS POEM

Christmas is coming, the wind is getting cold,
The sea is getting rough so I was told.
As I look out of my window
The grass is white,
Everything is covered, it's all out of sight
I get dressed, I go outside,
The snow is slippery, it's like a slide.
The sun comes up, it dries the snow away,
Today won't be as nice as yesterday.
I wake up, I go downstairs,
I'm the only one up, does nobody care?
Parcels open, parcels all for me
Stacked nicely under the Christmas tree.
I get stuck in, the paper's all on the floor,
What's Mum going to say,
Oh I'll shove it behind the door.
All the presents are opened,
It's all over, oh dear oh dear,
I can't wait for *Christmas next year!*

Louise Dalli (12)
Withernsea High School

YORKSHIRE PUDDING

Crispy brown puffs on a plate,
Gravy sinking through the Yorkshire pudding.
The lovely mixture turns into a crisp.

Stodgy, buttery smells coming from the oven,
Buttery puddings on the plate,
Waiting to be eaten.

Feeling a puff pastry is like feeling a Yorkshire pudding.
Yorkshire puddings feeling wet,
Flowing down a river of gravy.

Yorkshire puddings sliding down my mouth,
Yorkshire puddings, egg, flour and salt mixed with love,
Yorkshire puddings taste lovely!

Rachel Winter (12)
Withernsea High School

THE SEA

The sea is a mirror that reflects
all the beauty of the world.
The fish glide through it like arrows
in the Battle of Hastings.
The coral reefs are the delicacies
of God.
The sand is the sinking mud of
the amazon rainforest.
All the sharks guard the sea
like bouncers of night-clubs.
All the crustaceans surround the bed
like the ozone layer.
Oil continuously contaminates
all the living creatures of
the sea,
And yet still the sea is a mirror
that reflects all the beauty of the world.

James Thrippleton (12)
Withernsea High School

AUTUMN WORLD

It was cold last night,
of what I can remember,
but now it is morning and the leaves are falling.
I look outside and see piles of fallen leaves.
Now there is nothing left on the trees.
I get dressed all warm and cosy and walk
outside.
A cold pinch hits me on my nose,
and I smell the last scent of a fallen rose.
I can feel the crisp autumn breeze,
whistling around what's left of the trees.
A glimpse of sunlight reaches out,
to touch my eyes,
in-between the leaves of the trees.
It touches and the powerful beams hit my pupils,
my eyes close.
The sun goes back into its hiding place,
behind the candyfloss clouds.
My autumn world goes dark again,
as the sun travels to another autumn world
across the ocean.
I walk inside.
I turn back to see my last glimpse of autumn,
before the next turn of the rising sun.

Hannah Lockwood (12)
Withernsea High School

THE PLACE OF MEMORIES

The sound of the water echoing violently,
As it crashes against the misshapen rocks,
Tells a story of the agonising pain,
My heart's been through.
When I taste the salty sea
It reminds me how bitter I could be

So many memories I have of this place,
Some of which I choose not to have,
Maybe with time I'll forget them,
Then again maybe not.

Charline Grier (13)
Withernsea High School

ALL YEAR ROUND

January is bitter cold with lots of snow to throw.
February is still a bit cold but not much snow which
I can hold.
March is getting warmer, no more snow
or blustery winds.
April is the start of spring and it's the month my
birthday's in.
May is getting hotter, plant your plants and potter.
June is the time it's hot and summery, sunbathing
in your garden and eating your ice cream scrummily.
July is brilliant all hot and sweaty, you play with
your friends, talking and laughing.
August is starting to get cold, the rain draws in
and the night sky falls.
September is getting cold, get your gloves and woolly
hats on.
October is very chilly, especially in the morning when
the sun is dawning.
November is freezing and long cold winds circle you
in all directions.
December is *Christmas* yes! Yes! Lots of pressies round
your tree making you as excited as can be.

Carly Eldon (12)
Withernsea High School

COMPETITION WINNER

During the summer holidays,
We formed a lifestyle team,
The Village People was our name,
Working together was our theme.

We went to see the committee,
About the Memorial Hall,
Talked about doing the kitchen,
Buying curtains and painting it all.

We wanted to paint some animals,
On the playgroup wall,
We've done a horse with chickens and pigs,
And the children liked them all.

People donated paint and brushes,
And Focus gave us discount,
So we chose the kitchen units,
And brought the whole amount.

Writing up the log book,
Planning the next event,
Have we put up posters?
Are all reminders sent?

All the log books have been judged,
And we have got a chance,
To win a trip on a PGL,
To America or France.

Amy Goldspink (12)
Withernsea High School

THE HORRORS AT NIGHT

I wake up and find I've been dreaming,
My lights are down and the moon is gleaming.
My heart is pounding and I can't speak,
I look round the corner and take a peek,
He's coming, it's him, the man from the dead,
What he's coming to do, I fear to dread
I jump in bed and sneak under the cover,
I call out loud *'Mother, Mother'*
The lights are on, my mum has come,
My heart is still racing like the beat of a drum.
She holds me close and wipes my tears,
'Don't worry darling, Mum is here'
Now I look up and all is clear,
I was still dreaming, he was not here.
'Now go to sleep it's 2 o'clock'
Thank you Mum, thanks a lot.
Sweet dreams everyone.

Hannah Simpson (12)
Withernsea High School

THE SADNESS OF THE SWAN

She moves gracefully across the blue sparkling river,
Being aware of any strangers
Her neck in a shape of a broken love heart,
And her eyes so sad.
When she steps out onto the bank
She shakes and little pieces of water fly off.
Then she walks off to her place to sleep for the night,
To dream of her long-lost mate
Hoping that one day she will heal her broken heart.

Rebecca Aitchison (12)
Withernsea High School

THE FUTURE

As man goes further into the unknown,
Men are sacrificing their souls,
As we move further into the darkness
We will go to war,
For only war is the future of mankind,
As we are a violent race.

Michael Plant (12)
Withernsea High School

THE COLD NIGHT

One day it was a very cold night
So cold you could not feel yourself move.
I had to sit near the fire to keep myself warm.
I was scared because´you could hear whistling
And it was really windy.

Stephen Dale (13)
Withernsea High School

MY MUM

My mum is small
My mum is slim
She has brown hair
With brown eyes to match
But most of all
I like my mum
Because she loves me lots.

Victoria Hardy (12)
Withernsea High School

FIERY FIREWORKS

They rise like sudden fiery flowers
    That burst upon the night,
Then fall to earth in burning showers
    Of crimson, blue and white.

Like buds too wonderful to name
    Each miracle unfolds,
And Catherine wheels begin to flame
    Like whirling marigolds.

Rockets and Roman candles make
    An orchard of the sky,
Whence magic trees their petals shake
    Upon each gazing eye.

Stephanie Dee (12)
Withernsea High School

WHO AM I?

Who am I, a good question,
I am who I am,
The person I was born as,
I am my feelings, my mind, my actions,
I am what I do, where I come from,
I am my family background,
I am what I enjoy doing,
Places I like going,
I am I suppose in the end myself,
All I ever can be, all I ever will be.

Ben Fisher (14)
Withernsea High School

A Deadened Dark Scene

The land is murky and bare
The crisp autumn leaves lay
layer upon layer
The tall spiked trees stand
stripped naked
from their summer green
Leaving the land with a deadened
dark scene
The land is filled with chilling airs
The sun's sharp rays slash down
causing glares
The winter mists rise up from the damp
moist ground
Nothing can be heard, not one sound.

Kirsty Broom (13)
Withernsea High School

Seasons Of The Year

A utumn, the leaves are all crispy and brown
    and all frosted over.
U nder the damp, frosted over leaves,
    bugs are eating away at them.
T rees are bare, because all the leaves have
    fallen off.
U ncomfortably, the hedgehogs squirm as they
    are hibernating.
M um takes us to Hull fair, to go on all the
    biggest rides.
N ights get darker, the fireworks come out, and
    we all see them dancing in the sky.

Miriam Train (12)
Withernsea High School

DESERT ISLAND

It was once true that dinosaurs ruled
The sea reflects on the smooth sky,
And the twinkling sand sparkles in the sun.
Lizards scamper up and down trees,
Palm trees are rustling.
Coconuts are falling, hitting the sand with a thud.
The see-through sea is coming
And night is falling
Not much more time to find more fossils.

Jonathan Harper (13)
Withernsea High School

THE SEA

The sea crashes all day,
I don't want to get in its way,
The sea roars like a herd of wild boars,
It beats the cliff all day long,
The cliff can't take it, then soon it's gone.

Daniel Grantham (12)
Withernsea High School

AUTUMN

The crisp golden leaves whistle as they are swept along
by the beautiful silent wind.
The young children scuttle around
as the leaves slowly fall down
to the soft soil.
The children of God are not heard,
not a sound.

Robert Hunt (13)
Withernsea High School

WINTER

I woke up thinking of snow,
Nothing but snow.
I looked out of my window and gasped at the sight below
in the garden.
There, dazzling as the sun shone down on it was *snow!*
I leapt out of bed, dressed quickly and warmly,
Then dashed downstairs and into the garden.
At first I hesitated, not wanting to destroy the clean snow
on the ground before me.
But not for long,
Before you could say 'Pickled sausages'
I was dancing around the garden happily
Throwing snowballs at no one in particular.
I was standing in snow six inches deep,
Dressed in more than ten items of clothing,
Staring at miles of blinding white snow.
The crisp white snow was now covered in my footprints.
Darkness began to cover the sky, and
Unwillingly I trudged towards the house,
Shivering now that the sun had disappeared.
I undressed and climbed sleepily into bed.
It had been a long, long day, I thought as I lay down and
fell asleep.
I was asleep for only a few seconds,
I woke up and took one more glance outside at the snow,
But it had gone!
The garden, once covered with snow, was empty.
Not even a little bit of snow left.
It had just been a dream.

Philippa Cottrell (13)
Withernsea High School

POEM OF THE MONTHS

January is a time when children are
wrapped up warm in hats, scarves and gloves.
February is a time of romance, love hearts
and flowers, candlelight meals for two.
March is the beginning of spring, lambs jump
about in the fields, buds begin to grow on the trees.
April is a time of blossom and tricks on
April Fools' Day.
May is a time of warmer weather, butterflies
fluttering among the flowers.
June is a time for holidays and warmer weather,
July is a time when school breaks up for the long
summer holidays.
August is when crops ripen, golden in the fields,
Days are long and hot.
September is when kids go back to school
Fields are brown and ready to be sown.
October is a time of Hull fair, candyfloss,
brandy snap and toffee apples.
November is a time of cold dark mornings,
days are shorter.
Guy Fawkes' night awaits.
December is a time of excitement
Christmas trees, Christmas presents
and going to church.

Keith Stephenson (12)
Withernsea High School

MUMMY

Mummy is so lovely,
She feeds me at demand,
All I need to do is scream
And Mummy is at hand,
But when she pats me on the back
It feels like a punch,
So I keep my wind and pay her back
By bringing up my lunch.
Mummy is so fabulous
She's my number one.
My Dad's OK (let's just say)
He's clumsy with my bum
They say you cannot judge someone
You've not known very long,
Well I've known Mummy all my life
So I just can't be wrong!

Tara Murray (12)
Withernsea High School

LISTEN

Listen to the birds
Being killed by carelessness
Listen to the fish
Being polluted by us
Listen

Listen to the whales
As they are shot in the side
Listen to the mink
As they are skinned for fashion
Listen

Listen to the rainforest
As the areas are stripped
For housing for
People who pollute the world
Listen

Why don't we listen
To the things that
Have lived here for years
Listen.

Ellie Hailwood (13)
Withernsea High School

THE CHASE

The cheetah was stalking a young warthog,
While her cubs played near the muddy bog.

A crouched body and golden hair,
Her claws extended through flesh they will tear.
Creeping ever closer, still undetected,
The hog doesn't know, it's been selected.
On the hog she will pounce,
When she runs, she seems to bounce.

She and her family will eat the kill,
They will not stop until they have their fill.
With their mouths covered in blood,
A rest they will have, which will do them good.
From leopards and lions they will run,
But the next day, again they will hunt.

Andy Boothby (12)
Withernsea High School

MONDAY IS ...

Monday is magically made for maths and music,
Tuesday is tennis, outside in the courts,
Wednesday is wonderful for words; it's English,
Thursday is truly technical with technology,
Friday is Français; in English it's French,
Saturday is swimming, it's splashing with fun,
Sunday is superbly special, it's the day before
Monday.

James Place (12)
Withernsea High School

AUTUMN PICTURES

A utumn leaves brown and crisp,
U mbrellas come out for autumn showers.
T offee apples, hard and crispy,
U nder leaves hedgehogs hibernate.
M agnificent fireworks dance in the sky,
N ights close in as the days get shorter.

Stephen Norris (12)
Withernsea High School

INDOORS

Sitting by the fireside
With nothing to do
The flames are flickering
As the wood burns
I look outside and see
The cold rain trickle
Down the windowpane.

Matthew Blanchard (12)
Withernsea High School

HALLOWE'EN

On Hallowe'en night
People dress up to give you a fright
Ghosts and ghouls
Pumpkins with terror in their eyes
Nothing like the smell of fresh meat pies
People knocking on your door
Saying 'Trick or treat'
Don't be nasty
Open the door and give them something to eat.

Steven Wood (12)
Withernsea High School

ARE YOU ALRIGHT?

I'm up town with my mum,
She's miserable.
Are you alright?

I'm at my friend's house,
She's happy,
Are you alright?

I'm in my room with my dad,
He's tired,
Are you alright?

I'm stood over my dad's grave,
Crying in disbelief,
Are you alright Dad?

Amanda Ritchie (13)
Vermuyden School

CRAZY ALPHABET

A is for Adam who is a big daisy
B is for Brian who is very crazy
C is for Craig who has a big knife
D is for Danny who hasn't a life
E is for Emma who's as slow as a snail
F is for Felix who's as large as a whale
G is for Glen who plays with his toys
H is for Hayley who's after the boys
I is for Ian who speaks double Dutch
J is for Jamie who fidgets too much
K is for Kayleigh who never says thanks
L is for Lindsey who plans to rob banks
M is for Matthew who will pick his nose
N is for Natalie who stands on people's toes
O is for Oliver who won't wash his face
P is for Philip who cheats in a race
Q is for Queenie who is a big swat
R is for Robert who lives in a cot
S is for Steven who's good in the net
T is for Tanya who likes being wet
U is for Una who bellows and bawls
V is for Vicky who scribbles on walls
W is for William who plays with his rattles
X is for Xena who can fight her battles
Y is for Yorick it's nearly the end
Z is for Zak who's a very good friend.

David Locke (13)
Vermuyden School

ALL MY LOVE'S FOR YOU

I sit by the phone,
but you never call.
I wait, wait and wait,
all my love's for you.

I sit by the door,
but you never knock.
I wait, wait and wait,
all my love's for you.

I sit in the park,
but you never come.
I wait, wait and wait,
all my love's for you.

Sarah Hewson (13)
Vermuyden School

POEM

I wondered what to write
With a puzzled look on my face
Searching the classroom for inspiration
But to my disappointment no avail.
I started to get angry
It swelled up in my soul
But then suddenly it hit me
To write about it,
Yes I would write about that
My best idea, first to my brain
I would write about . . .

John Johnson (14)
Vermuyden School

PEOPLE CALL ME . ..

People call me thick,
I don't know why.
Maybe it's because,
I tried talking to a fly.

People call me weird,
I don't know why.
When people come up to me,
I go all shy.

People call me mad,
I don't know why.
Just because I talk,
about the way people die.

People call me soft,
I don't know why.
When my mum leaves,
I usually cry.

People call me brain dead,
I don't know why
I get things wrong,
but I try, try, try.

People call me daft,
I don't know why.
Just because I ask,
Who painted the sky.

People call me clever,
I don't know why.
Sometimes I think they must,
be telling a lie.

People call me stupid,
I don't know why.
I jumped under a train,
now I know what it's,

Like to die.

Steven Hicks (14)
Vermuyden School

IMAGINE A WORLD

Imagine a world with destruction and greed,
as weak as a withering weed.
Imagine a world with no clean air,
oxygen is very rare.
Imagine a world with no poverty or wars,
a world with no laws.
Imagine a world without any light,
darkness forever, with lack of sight.
Imagine a world with non-stop crime,
a housebreak, a robbery within a second of time.
Imagine a world without any flowers,
no need for sunshine, no need for showers.
Imagine a world without any fashion,
no special clothes, no love, no passion.
Imagine a world without bacteria,
no need for major diseases like listeria.
Imagine a world without a fear or worry,
no need for phobias, no need to worry.
Imagine a world without the ability to read,
Poetry wouldn't be a major need.

Sean Lilley (13)
Vermuyden School

I HATED IT!

You always used to laugh at me
You always used to cry
You were never there
I hated it!

You used to go away
and never say goodbye
I would stay alone and cry
I hated it!

You said to me I was the one
but you lied
You said you would be there for me
but you weren't
I hated it!

You said I could tell you anything
but you told the town
I thought I could trust you
but I couldn't
I hated it!

Samantha Hobson (13)
Vermuyden School

HORSES

If I had a wish I would wish for a horse,
One with four legs of course.
With a flowing tail and a mane that glows
We could go to places that nobody knows.

Lisa Shipley (13)
Vermuyden School

WE'D ALWAYS BE TOGETHER

I used to see myself,
Next to you every day.
We did the same thing,
Laughed in the same way.

We'd always be together.

We had similar clothes,
And thought quite the same.
If we did anything wrong,
You were to blame.

We'd always be together.

I now walk down the street,
All empty and upset.
I feel like part of me has died,
The one I will never forget.

We will be together,
Some day.

Ruth Broughton (13)
Vermuyden School

THE MOON

The moon is not always full,
Sometimes it looks like a thread of silver,
Sometimes it looks like a banana
Or a wedge of cheese.
But the moon is not really changing
It is always the same shape.

Simon Locke (12)
Vermuyden School

THE BATTLEFIELD

The battlefield is so bloody
all around
The battlefield is so gory
even in your mind
In every sound the cry of
soldiers echo
The sounds of guns crackle
in the distance
Soldiers going down around
the battlefield
The views of enemies charging towards you
charging, charging, charging.

Andrew Woolass (13)
Vermuyden School

BOYZONE

I'm so glad I'm a Boyzone fan,
Stephen is my main man,
Then there's Shane, who's BMX mad,
Followed by Keith, he's quite a lad,
Mikey's next, but he's my second best,
Boyzone are the best.

Ronan's the one that I missed out,
His singing is something to talk about,
Dublin is their home town,
They all deserve a golden crown.
Please forget the rest,
Boyzone are the best.

Poppy Bolton (13)
Vermuyden School

HE NEVER CAME BACK

My brother went to Vietnam,
When I was a little boy.
He must have liked it there,
Because he never came back.

My brother went to Vietnam.
He wrote a letter everyday.
He must be very busy there.
The letters stopped coming,
And he never came back.

My brother went to Vietnam,
My mother tells me about him.
I ask her where he is.
She says he likes it there
Because he never came back.

My brother went to Vietnam,
Some day I'm going to meet him.
The brother I grew up without,
Because he never came back.

My brother went to Vietnam.
He died in Vietnam.
I lived alone,
In one big lie,
Because he never came back.

Adam Price (13)
Vermuyden School

I WANT TO BE . . .

I want to be a rockstar
with long spiky hair
I want to be a pilot
gliding through the air

I want to be a lifeguard
swimming in the sea
I want to be a monkey
climbing up a tree

I want to be a teacher
giving some detentions
I want to be an inventor
making some inventions

I want to be an actor
and star in a play
I want to be Santa
and ride upon a sleigh

I want to be hairdresser
doing ladies' perms
I want to be a gardener
digging up some worms

I want to have a baby
and change its dirty nappy
I don't care what I am
as long as I am happy.

Vikki Grant (12)
Vermuyden School

MY LOVE FOR YOU IS EVERLASTING

I love you,
I love you so much, that nothing will stop it.
I could be anywhere and still love you.
If I was dying I would still love you.
Death would be but a line. Because I love you.
My love for you would shatter that line into pieces.
If that line didn't break, my heart would.

I love you,
If you left me, for months, I would cry.
But I would still love you.
Without you
I don't know
What
I would do,
Because . . .
Because . . .
I love you.
I love you so much,
And all I would
Ever,
Ever,
Want from you is
A kiss.

Robert Hague (14)
Vermuyden School

WERE YOU THERE?

Friends were picking on me,
Think about it,
Were you there?

I was having a hard time,
Think about it,
Were you there?

A member of my family was dying,
Think about it,
Were you there?

It's Christmas time
Presents all around
Were you there?
Yes, you were there.

Isn't it funny,
You're there when you want things,
But when you are needed,
You're never there.

Hayley Chiswell (13)
Vermuyden School

DONNIE DIDN'T DUCK!

We were out playing cricket
I chucked him the ball
'Duck' I shouted but . . .
Donnie didn't duck!

We were out playing football
I chucked him the ball
'Duck' I shouted but . . .
Donnie didn't duck!

We were out playing baseball
I chucked him the ball
'Duck' I shouted but . . .
Donnie didn't duck!

I had a friend
But he won't play ball
And all because
Donnie didn't duck!

Michael Smith (13)
Vermuyden School

MY BROTHER

My brother does nothing but annoy my mother,
He plays all day,
In his own special way,
I definitely don't want another.
He's not always bad,
But he still drives me mad,
He's always getting in bother.
I suppose he can be nice,
When I pay the price,
We're completely different from each other.
The thing that annoys me most, is . ..
He's the one that makes the mess,
Then he's the one who tidies the less.
He would be nice if he wasn't so bad,
If he changed, I would be glad.
I can't go on, the list would be too long,
So I'll stop right here,
Before he comes near.

Lucy Pollard (11)
Vermuyden School

PARADISE

All around me I see the bright sparkling sun,
glaring into my eyes.
Set on my body giving me the dark brown tan
that I've always wanted.
I see the flash of mystery in the light blue ocean.
I see the soft, silky sand surrounding me.
As I walk across the sand my feet sink deep,
I feel the grains in-between my toes.
I can hear the palm trees swaying in the cool sea breeze,
I see the shadow of the trees on the beach.
I feel free and calm.
I hear a soft bang and there laying beside me
is an open coconut.
As I drink the milk, I feel it run down my throat
and I get a slight shiver down my spine.
This is my idea of paradise,
but as I come back to reality the bright sun
is the classroom lights.
The blue ocean is the sea of people
sat in front of me and the large palm tree
is of course Miss Hendrix standing over me.
Oh well it's nice to dream.

Adele Smithson (13)
Vermuyden School

PARK

The park is fun and exciting,
Lots of people go and have fun.
Swings, roundabouts, slides,
Climbing frames and swinging bridges.
John, Jayne and Jenni play tag,
Tig you're on!

Sometimes people play football.
Lots of people join in with the tig game.
Parks have different things.
'I'm the king of the castle and you're the dirty rascal'
That's the famous saying.

Jayne Storey (11)
Vermuyden School

THE TIGER

Tiger Tiger
Eyes so bright
Shining at me
In the night

Will he jump?
Will he pounce?
I stand so still
I dare not move

Quick as a flash
The tiger pounces
Slowly I edge backwards
He stops

He eyes me up
With his beady eyes
He turns round
And slowly walks away

I very carefully
And quietly
Walked away
And never went there again.

Ryan Gamewell (11)
Vermuyden School

BONFIRE NIGHT

Crackling wood on the fire
The children everywhere
Their faces light up with glee
As rockets go up in the air
Oh what's that bang?
The sky is full with light
Because tonight is Bonfire night
The smell of toffee, hot dogs and soup
Everyone keeps warm round the fire
Mum cooks chestnuts round the fire
While Dad checks the fireworks in the box
Red, orange and green
A traffic light is what I've seen
Dad's in charge, he lights them
Right, because tonight there's
Always danger on Bonfire night.

Paul Martin (11)
Vermuyden School

LIVING IN A CAGE

What would it feel like to live in a cage?
Would you feel like you're on stage?
People walk by just to see,
Other people looking at me.
Then they decide to stop and stare,
To join the people who are already there.
Would you feel trapped and insecure?
Or maybe that you're just obscure?
What would it be like to live in a cage?
I guess I'll never know.

Lynsey Charles (13)
Vermuyden School

THE SHADOWS LOOMED AROUND ME

There I lay in darkness, seven years of age,
Shadows loomed around me, calling me by my name,
I screamed and yelled and shouted, but no one seemed to hear,
But all the shapes around me, laughed with a dreadful sneer.

Not a clue to do had I, but to lay there and shake,
As the shapes around me, come nearer as I wait,
The shadows seemed to laugh, at my showing fright,
And closer to my bed they came, turning me quite white.

Just as I was at fainting point, my foot touched something hard,
'My torch!' I thought with sudden joy, and grabbed it pretty quick,
I turned it on in triumph, as the light shone across the room!

The things, they disappeared, as my light hit them,
And clutching my torch tightly, I laid down my sleepy head,
Goodnight rotten shadows, won't see you again,
As long as I have my torch, you won't haunt me again!

Charlotte Marston (11)
Vermuyden School

DREAMING AGAIN

The team sheet went up, and there my name
was at number two.
I could imagine pulling on the number two jersey
and walking down the tunnel
to hear the crowd shouting out my name,
'Collins, Collins, Collins.' It went on.
'Steven, Steven wake up.'
Now the dream starts again.

Steven Collins (13)
Vermuyden School

SPOTS

You squeeze
them
you pick
them
you do whatever
you can to get rid of them
they're big and yellow with
puss inside and when you
get one you need to hide
and after you squeeze
them you feel sick inside
but look at your finger
to see what a find!

Samantha Hale (14)
Vermuyden School

THE ONE THAT GOT AWAY

My favourite sport is fishing.
To catch the biggest pike I am wishing.
But my dreams never seem to come true.
The big one always seems to get away
To fight another angler another day.
He seems to laugh and say you can't catch me any day.

With a wiggly worm upon my hook
I hope this will change my luck.
I sit and wait all day long
But the fish don't seem to be feeding anyway.

Stuart Stow (13)
Vermuyden School

YOU SAID

I'll be there when you need me
you said
but were you?
No.

I'll take care of you always
you said
but did you?
No.

When you have a problem you can tell me
I'll listen
but did you?
No.

Whenever you said you'd be there
you weren't
you never had time for me.

Nicola Sykes (13)
Vermuyden School

RIP

Though you're gone
You're always here
I feel you close
You're in my tear.
This may seem cruel
But I am glad you've gone
'Cause you're not in pain
That makes me happy.
I shall see you again
Once I've lived my life.

Hannah Frances Bennett (13)
Vermuyden School

TIME TO GO TO THE DENTIST

I walked in
    and
lots of people were waiting
    nobody talked
It must be bad
So I sat down
with everybody looking at me thinking I'm mad for
    smiling
The dentist came out
    'Heidi
The room on your left
    Open up'
    Argh!
So I came out
    with
faces grinning at me
    It was bad.

Heidi Epton (13)
Vermuyden School

AUTUMN

All the time seasons change
light to dark, warm to cold.
The leaves flutter to the ground
with colours of red, gold and brown.
We pack our summer clothes away
and wrap up warm, fire's on,
curtains closed and we are cosy inside
thinking of warm places to be.

Natalie Spavin (13)
Vermuyden School

THE GOAL

It's my first day of football training
Will I score?
Will I make the team?
'Bang'
The ball's at my feet what should I do?
" 'Liam switch it'
'Cross it Liam'
'Shoot, shoot'
Bang, the ball's in the air please go in smack it's hit the crossbar
'Oh' chested it bang it's gone in
'Goal'
Will that be the goal that puts me on the team?
Please, please let me be on the team.

Liam Hoier (13)
Vermuyden School

MY TEDDY BEAR

Is he real?
Or is he false?
Can he see?
Or is he blind?
Does he watch me?
Or does he stare?
Can he talk?
Or can he walk?
Does he change colour?
Or does he stay brown?
Does he get scared when I play my music?
Don't cry teddy bear
You are mine!

Kaley Munday (11
Vermuyden School

LOVE HURTS

You meet for the first time,
He loves me,
He hates me,
You hold hands under the moonlight,
He loves me,
He hates me,
You kiss under the stars.
He loves me,
He hates me,
You go to dinner,
He loves me,
He hates me,
He drives away with his cases packed,
He hates me.

Sophie Howard (13)
Vermuyden School

FOOTBALL POEM

As I walked out of the tunnel
with my number eleven shirt on my back
and the crowd screaming
'Come on you blues'
'Come on you blues'
We had to win to win the league,
just one win
It went 1-0 then 2-0 then 3-0
At full time we lost 3-0,
but we won the league anyway.

Lee Gelder (13)
Vermuyden School

THE BARE TREE

The bare tree it wavers in the wind,
silently swaying
like a sobbing angel over a
stranger's death bed.
Creaking, wailing, crying with sadness,
at the loss of its children
that lay fatefully on the ground,
being slowly eaten by scavengeous microbes,
under the canopy of arms
of their old mother,
the one that fed them until their plight.
As autumn fell
the tree again felt anguish
at the loss of its many offspring.
But with a silent hope,
the tree gives a sombre smile,
In the form of a stance
holding its arms high and proud
towards the sky,
as it guards its future children
for the summer ahead by nurturing them
in her bed of tree sap.
And keeping them warm with her harsh bark
that is wound around her delicate frame
making her look strong
while she waits for the sun to shine
bright is that her children can dance
and wave and enjoy the bliss
of their short-lived lives.

Emma Credland (15)
Vermuyden School

LOVE POEM TO YOU

L ove is a special thing between me and you.
O nly you could make my heart melt.
V arious things brought us together.
E veryone said you're like Leonardo DiCaprio.

P eople say we were made for each other.
O nly you could break my heart.
E very time I do something wrong, you always forgive me.
M um and Dad can't wait for the wedding.

T ogether we can make it last.
O nly you could forgive me for the things I've done to you.

Y ou love me and I love you.
O ur love can never be parted.
U can always cheer me up when I am down.

Lisa Mapplebeck (14)
Vermuyden School

LOST IN SNOW AND NOWHERE TO GO

My hands were cold my feet were freezing and I was lost in snow,
The fog was thick the sky was white with a continuing glow,
The snow stopped falling the clouds started clearing and the fog
                                        then disappeared,
I saw my house and ran towards it with happiness and relief,
My dog ran for me and her welcome was more than brief,
Then I walked inside and sat next to the fire,
I warmed my hands and warmed my feet and slowly fell asleep.

Simon Standring (12)
Vermuyden School

THE WORDSMITH

You dance round my thoughts, a pure inspiration,
With your silk sheen gown and your cobwebbed shoes,
And I think to myself as you stand silently in my mind's eye,
'I wish I could know who you are.'

'I am a wordsmith, a poet, an author,
Working words of clay into objects of beauty,
Turning streams of thoughts into flowing rivers of emotional words,
Listening to whispers of trees and fern,
Waiting for the time when the dew descends,
To capture the pictures inside my head.'

I notice you as I sleep in my dreamland,
With your pale slender neck and your ribbons of rainbows,
And I whisper softly as the dawn light beckons,
'I wish I could know who you are.'

'I am a wordsmith, a poet, an author,
Working words of clay into objects of beauty,
Turning streams of thoughts into flowing rivers of emotional words,
Watching the moonlight in a starry glade,
Waiting for the sunrise,
To capture the feelings of natural presence.'

I see you again, so shrouded in mystery,
With your dark shining head and your mystical eyes,
And I say out aloud, for you fill me with wonder,
'I have to know who you are!'

'I am a wordsmith, a poet, an author,
Working words of clay into objects of beauty,
Turning streams of thoughts into flowing rivers of emotional words,
I would die if I could not drink the birds' song,
But I'll live forever, and ever, and always,
On the planet of words and eternal dreams.'

Emily Harding (11)
Vermuyden School

THEY'RE LEAVING, THEY'RE GONE!

He had finished school
She was leaving
He had left
She was leaving today
He
She had grown-up so quick
He had grown-up so fast
Why?
It wasn't long ago
Why is she leaving
He had spoken
No!
His first
Don't let her
Word
Go!

Julie Stainton (13)
Vermuyden School

OUTSIDE

Outside it's a lazy hot day
and leaves are falling off the trees at random
for a glance at the ground.

Outside the ground is covered with
muddy green grass with a sparkling reflection
from the sun.

Outside the sun is sparkling on
everything that you can see and more.

William Chatham (11)
Vermuyden School

HEARTACHE!

I thought that I never
really loved you,
but until we parted
all I could feel was
        heartache!

I watched you with her,
dreamt I was her,
longing to be her, but
all I could feel was
        heartache!

I hoped that you'd
love me too, in my mind,
all I could feel was
        heartache!

I see you with her,
I see you talking with her,
But all you give me is
        heartache!

Emma Blacker (13)
Vermuyden School

ONE WINDY DAY

It was one cold and windy day in winter
The trees were blowing
The leaves were falling
And the animals were hiding
Cans were blowing along the streets
And slates ripping off roofs
Trees were falling onto the crowds.

Lee Barker (11)
Vermuyden School

NIGHT-TIME

Nightmares approaching my silent head
Peaceful, relaxing, laying in bed.
Shooting stars break open the sky,
Slowly the night is passing by.
Spots of light reflecting around,
My heart is fearfully starting to pound.
Twinkling stars, they're already out,
Scary noises, I start to shout.
Moonlight shining in through the gaps,
Insects crawling in my bed, perhaps.
My eyelids heavy, they're beginning to tire,
Thinking will there be a big fire?
Within a flash I'm fast asleep,
Until morning not to peep.
Dreaming of the night-time ghosts,
Who suck your blood and then do boast.
Hearing noises in my head,
Dad is shouting 'Get out of bed.
Night-time's over once again,
Feeling relieved to be back, sane.

Kimberley Leckenby (12)
Vermuyden School

MY PUPPY DOG

I've got a dog and her name is Lilly
She's as soft as a brush and is very silly.
I look after her every day
And she will never ever refuse to play.
I take her for a walk to the park
And we have fun and she will sometimes bark.

Katie Hodgson (11)
Vermuyden School

TELETUBBIES

Tinky Winky, Dipsy, Laa-Laa and Po,
All stand on their toes.
Tinky Winky's purple
Dipsy's green
Laa-Laa's yellow
And Po's red
They all sleep in little small beds.
Tinky Winky has a handbag
Dipsy has a hat
Laa-Laa has a ball
And Po has a scooter.
The noisy hoover Noo-Noo goes around
cleaning up all the Tubby custard and Tubby toast.
All the children like to watch them on the television.

Laura Whiteley (13)
Vermuyden School

ROLLER-COASTER

Going high going low
Going fast as it will show.
I'm in my seat not knowing what to do.
What if we get to the top and I'm sick on you?
Going round and round and round.
Oh no watch out we're going to hit the ground.
Oh no, *aghh phew.*
We almost hit the queue.
I sit there staring at the track
And I know there's no turning back.

Chris Pollard (11)
Vermuyden School

NATURE

Frogs shimmering as they come out of the water,
Watery slime of a snail's foot glistens on the path.

Trees rustle and leaves soar in the wind,
Wind howls in the air on a cold day.

Plants so shiny and silky when they are in the sun,
Sun when it's going down into the sea.

Green pieces of grass stand upright on the ground,
Ground as hard as a cold stone.

Everything growing and changing every day,
Day after day as time goes by.

Christopher Smithson (11)
Vermuyden School

MY DOG

I have a dog she has a fluffy tail and big brown eyes,
She likes being fussed she has a good-nature.
She is a very good and bright dog
Her pointed ears can hear danger,
She is calm, still and quiet.

She is extremely confident of herself.
She is the best dog anyone could have.

Shane Tavinder (11)
Vermuyden School

WAITING AT THE DENTIST

It's not that bad
sat in total silence
listening to the drill
with people crying

and

People sat still
chewing gum
as if they were waiting for important test results.
Sat as if they were gonna die.

But . . .

It's not that bad at all
until your name was called
knowing that the drill is
going to be in our mouth

But then again . . .

It's just the dentist.

Melanie Hodgson (13)
Vermuyden School

A TIGER

A sadness deep in his eyes,

T he beautiful striped tiger,
I s crying inside.
G reat creature of orange and black,
E nergetic, endangered species of cat,
R emembering times of freedom past.

Emma Raywood (11)
Vermuyden School

FOLDERS

What's the point in folders?
all the brainy kids have the
Just so their work doesn't get creased
But gets to stay tidy
so they get loads of merits.
Ohhh! If I ever find out who made folders
I'll ring his neck with a hook
I'll give him a wave
Kick him up the bum

laugh and run.
At last I got rid of all the folders
and all the paper of the brainy kids was
Creased
Yahoo!
all the merits started to drop
Woohoo!

Nicholas Hobson (12)
Vermuyden School

THE VIEW FROM MY WINDOW

Flailing, rustling trees, waving to passers-by
Rippling, flowing waters, leading ships to their destination
An anchor, dedicated to all those who put their lives in peril
                                        with the water
Dogs, sniffing every tree they pass
Bushes rustling and swaying with the wind
Cars and vans representing all trades rushing by
People, usually with umbrellas, hurrying by to do their weekly shop

Rebecca Hunter (11)
Vermuyden School

HOLIDAY

Bump

> We're moving
> Not long to go
> Until I'm on the beach
> in Spain

Roar

> There goes the engine
> But what if we crash
> Will we take off?
> Will we arrive?

Bump

> What's wrong?
> We've stopped
> Oh just waiting
> for clearance

Roar

> Ahh what's happening?
> I'm begin sucked back
> I'm tilting back
> Please take off

Whoosh

> We're up in the air
> I'm flying
> I'm feeling sick
> *Bleau!*

Michael Hague (13)
Vermuyden School

THE EARTH

A pearly green, marble rolls in space.
Twirling and spreading secrets.

The white fluffy clouds
Swirl and curl.
From up here it looks like
A sphere
Hanging in space.

It is dazzling like
Sapphires, Emeralds of blue
Green mountains of gold.

But when we look closely
At starvation, selfishness
Pollution,
People having just a few
Grains of rice.

The world isn't as
Beautiful as we think.
Pollution in rivers kills.
Selfishness starts wars.

Amy Risebury (12)
Vermuyden School

CHRISTMASTIME

Christmastime will soon be here.
Making us happy every year.
Lots of things for girls and boys,
Sack upon sack of lovely toys.

Christmas trees and holly too,
Bringing joy from me to you.
Christmas cards cover the walls,
With mistletoe hanging in the halls.

Carol singers at the door
Announcing Christ's birth to rich and poor.
Lanterns shining, faces aglow,
Standing in the cold, cold snow.

Soon it will be Christmas Day,
When we can laugh and be really gay.
For everyone is happy, it's that time of year,
To welcome each other from far and near.

Anne Morris (12)
Vermuyden School

RED, RED, ROSE

Love is like a red, red rose
So sweet and warm and gentle
The colours are so beautiful
Red are my favourite
If ever I get one it will be a miracle.
So be my miracle my red, red rose.

Love is like a red, red rose
So tender and calm and warm
The petals are like pastel colours
White is my favourite too
If ever I get my hands on one it will be a miracle.
So be my miracle my red, red rose.

Love is like a red, red rose
So colourful and powerful
They smell as sweet as perfume
I also like peach, pink and yellow
February the 14th will be worth living
If I get a Valentine rose.
So be my miracle my red, red rose.

Kirsty Stephenson (13)
Vermuyden School

STICKS AND STONES

Sticks and stones will break my bones
But names'll never hurt me,
Maybe a sting from a bumble bee,
That's what'll hurt me.
Maybe not a woman called Dee,
Maybe not a shopping fee,
That wouldn't hurt me.
Maybe if I fell off a big tree,
Maybe someone flicking a pea,
Or someone shouting in my ear 'Yippee!'
That's what might hurt me.

Gary Bray (11)
Vermuyden School

CLASSROOM MANIA

Sticking licking bubblegum flicking.
Rubbers flying aeroplanes gliding.
Amy for Chris and Chris for Amy.
Blackboard screeching.
Children screaming.
Everybody shouting.
Teachers coming.

Fay Gibson (11)
Vermuyden School

BUT YOU DIDN'T

Remember the time when you
lent me your bike
and it got nicked
I thought you'd kill me
but you didn't

Remember the time I was going to lend
you some money for the shop
and I forgot
I thought you'd hate me
but you didn't
you forgave me.

Darren Bussey (13)
Vermuyden School

NON-SMOKERS ARE THE BEST

Smoking is bad
Smoking is sad
Don't smoke your life away
And you will be glad
It will make you smell
Like a dirty old car
So use your head
And stay fresh
Non-smokers are the best.

Michael Leyland (11) & Kerry Leyland (12)
Vermuyden School

UNTITLED

Let me be your Titanic
I will never sink
Let me be your clothes
I will never shrink
If you like your clothes warm
Let me be your heater
You call the shots
I wanna be yours.

Ben Brinded (13)
Vermuyden School

THE MAN I KNEW

The man I knew I will never forget.
He lived in our shed
And he came from Tibet.
He had a tattoo on his arm.
He was very tall.
His hair was black and his name was Paul.
He eats steel for breakfast
And you should see his lunch,
All washed down with a big fruit punch.
But I'll never forget him, well just a bit,
Because I thought him up.

Thomas Donnelly (11)
Vermuyden School

THE NIGHT IS . . .

The night is,
Car headlights turned on,
Street lights getting brighter,
House alarms getting set,
Bedroom lights turning on and off,
Crickets scratching legs,
Frogs croaking, cats miaowing,
Dogs growling,
Bats flapping wings.

David Dodgson (12)
Vermuyden School

COME WITH ME

Roses are red
  Violets are blue
You're so pretty I love you
  The sea is blue
The sky is white
  So you should come with me tonight
Wood is brown
  The sun is yellow
You saw me and I said 'Hello'
  Coal is black
Blood is red
  Come upstairs with me to bed.

Wayne Ransome (14)
Vermuyden School

CHIPS AND PEAS

Chips are very nice
Buy them from a chip shop
I always buy them with peas
Very very delicious
Had them last night
Made me have a fight
They give me hunger
And made me stronger
If you always get beat up
Eat the hungry chips
They will give you a hunger
Beautiful wonderful chips.

Leon Hudson (11)
Vermuyden School

THE FRIGHTENING NIGHT

Running up the stairs,
Shutting the bedroom door,
Closing the curtains tightly,
Racing across the floor.

I jump in bed just before midnight,
Before the witches and the bogeymen come
Out to haunt me in my sleep.
The clock strikes twelve,
I close my eyes,
Before the night gives me a terrible fright.

In my dreams I see my fears,
I try to escape but it's useless.
I can't get away but I try and try,
Then all of a sudden I'm in my bed,
Ready to start the new day ahead.

Daniel Bowling (11)
Vermuyden School

THE WAY I DO BABY

As you walk away without a word or goodbye
I've just got this feeling and I just want to die
Nobody loves you the way I do baby
Nobody needs you the way I do baby
When you see me crying you turn round and walk my way
Sit yourself beside me and wipe my tears away
Nobody loves you the way I do baby
Nobody needs you the way I do baby.

Ryan Johnson (14)
Vermuyden School

FIVE

Five are on
the stage
Abs
Scott
Rich
'J'
and
Sean
My throat is sore
sore from
screaming

They dance so good
I wish I could stay
here
forever
They sang
'Everybody Get Up'
and
'Got the Feelin''
It's so
brill
to be
here
watching
Five,
Five come
alive!

Lauren Chessman (13)
Vermuyden School

But You Don't

I tell you to put the rubbish out
but you don't

I tell you to put the car in the garage
but you don't

I tell you to do the washing up
but you don't

Is it that bad
I don't ask much
I just want a little help

I tell you to get the snow off the path
you did a bit

I tell you to wrap up
but you don't

I tell you to get up
but you don't

It was that bad
I asked a lot
I just wanted a bit too much help.

Antony Partington (13)
Vermuyden School

The Loud Teacher

The loud teacher wears masks,
He gives us loads of hard tasks,
He also wears a cloak of black,
And knocks on the door with a
Rat-a-tat-tat.

The loud teacher wears masks,
He gives us cabbage for our snack,
He also is a big fat grump,
And knocks on he door with a
Rat-a-tat-thump.

Amanda Allen (11)
Vermuyden School

HEAVEN!

Up in the clear clouds,
Among the wind and rain,
Up in the hands of God,
Is where you'll feel no pain,

It's safe up there,
There's angels around,
Don't fear about dying,
You'll be safe and sound.

Everything is free,
Just like your dreams,
You float away,
On the heavenly streams.

Where is this place?
I want to know!
So when I die,
I'll be able to go!

Now I'm here,
Up in heaven,
You realise you really are
And every night you fall asleep on your special star!

Hayley Watson (13)
Vermuyden School

The Stranger

He came through the door
Looking for a table.
Slowly he walked
Towards the table.
He sat down quickly
And took his hat off from his head
And placed it on the bench.
Slowly he raised
His hand
And
Clicked his fingers
Waiting for the waiter
To approach.

Craig Challenger (13)
Vermuyden School

My Love Poem

M y love is for you and only you
Y our lovely blue eyes

L ong golden hair
O ther people can say goodbye
V iolin music is as soft as your sweet voice
E ventually you will see what you mean to me

P revailing winds blow me deeper into your heart
O ther days I used to cry and say 'Why oh why'
E very day I think of you for all 24 hours
M y love for you is deep as the deep deep sea.

Mark Biggs (13)
Vermuyden School

LOVE

I see him at the corner,
Waiting for his bus,
He's never noticed me,
As he's always in a rush,
I love the way his hair shines,
Kinks and curls around,
His eyes sparkling brightly,
Like diamonds in the ground,
I only hope that one day,
His eyes will meet mine,
And then I will be happy,
For a very long long time.

Leanne Harness (13)
Vermuyden School

I 'ATE THE DARK!

I 'ate the dark,
It's scary,
Monsters come out in dark,
I 'ate 'em,
I really do,
I 'ate the dark,
It's 'orrible,
It's just the dark,
People gerrin off in streets,
Me and me lad walking alone in dark,
Coppers everywhere in the dark,
It's just 'orrible is the dark.

Samantha Ehlers (12)
Vermuyden School

SCHOOL

S chool is scary
C old in the classroom
H aunted in the hall
O ur teacher is Mrs Hall
O h no we've got history next
L earning is not the best.

David Fielder (11)
Vermuyden School

BONFIRE NIGHT

Today's the day, Bonfire night,
The screaming of the fire,
The bangs in the air,
Guy Fawkes is coming, coming to scare.
Bonfire night, the hissing fire blaze.
Bonfire night, kids screaming,
What is Bonfire night,
No one knows.

Jade Morton (11)
Vermuyden School

NIGHT IS . . .

Night is cold
Night is dark
Night is when you don't play in the park.

Night is when there is no light.
Night is the opposite to day
Night is when the bats come out to *play!*

Samantha Croley (11)
Vermuyden School

THE TIME WE MET

Love is forever till death us do part.
We share out our love which comes from the heart.
The best kind of love is when two become one.
Without holding each other life cannot go on.

Love is two people who care for each other,
Sharing everything there is together.
Through thick and thin they both go.
Even when one is feeling low.

Love is two hearts going into one,
Colliding with angels singing a song.
It was fate that brought us together,
I will remember the time we met, forever.

Sarah Ledger (13)
Vermuyden School

THE BROKEN WORLD

The essence of the world is fading away
amongst the mist of extinction it's weeping astray.
Its elegant form and motion is as
tender and slender as the flowing ocean.
The melodies that made our Earth are
broken up into hard dirt and earth.
Mankind came and took its mother,
soon it will be gone and we don't even bother.
We don't give a glance.
We don't give a thought,
that one day our world will be broken,
dreary and distraught.

Jade Shaw (14)
Vermuyden School

THE DENTIST'S RIDE

Opening the door
as someone comes out
I go in.
I sit down and wait
the clock strikes three
and goes ding-dong, ding-dong
I look around
people moving
going upstairs.
My name was called
I follow someone
I sit down in the chair
and it gave me the ride of my life.
I opened wide
and decided to shout
because I was about
to cough.
The ride had stopped
that was the end.

Anthony Carter (14)
Vermuyden School

IF ONLY

If only I never did it
I would still have you
If only there was something that I could only do
To show you how much I love you
And hope that you would love me too
Then I would be happy instead of being blue.

Emma Denford (13)
Vermuyden School

Rainbow

(Dedicated To Dee)

I'm walking on a rainbow,
I'm floating in the sky.
I'm walking on a rainbow,
I do not frown or sigh.

I'm walking on a rainbow,
I'm gliding through the air.
I'm walking on a rainbow,
I do not give a care.

I'm walking on a rainbow,
I'm turning round a bend.
I'm walking on a rainbow,
I know I'll reach the end.

Louisa Gibb (13)
Vermuyden School

Love Hurts

L ost in the depth of your eyes
O pening my heart with your voice
V oice of an angel that sings
E ver - forever I'm yours

H urting my love is for you
U ntolled hurt you gave in return
R uthless your actions to me
T orment is all that you give
S orrow is all that you bring.

Emma Johnson (13)
Vermuyden School

REMEMBERING THE TIME

Remember the time you invited
your boss to tea?
The house looked like a bomb dropped
I thought you'd go mad.
But you didn't!

Remember the time it was my birthday
you bought me a card.
I thought you would get me a present.
But you didn't!

Remember the time we went to the fair
I went on a ride with another man.
I thought you'd go mad.
But you didn't!

I thought we were going to get married
because I loved you so much,
I was waiting for you to ask.
If you loved me too because I loved you
and I thought you would meet me
at the church.
But you didn't!

Leanne Preston (14)
Vermuyden School

BROKEN HEARTS

Broken hearts come from love
One minute you're happy
The next you're not.
It's a man who breaks your heart
So forget it all and walk out.

Broken hearts will soon mend
One day you're sad,
The next you're not.
It's the tissues you waste,
On that one man you once loved.

Gemma Robinson (13)
Vermuyden School

BYE BYE SCHOOL

It's half-past three,
Nearly time for tea,
Dringg! First to the school gates.
Got to be me,
I get home to watch TV,
Then all of a sudden,
It hits me,
Should I have left that fag
In the science lab
with all the gas taps turned on?
Then up comes the news,
The school has blown up,
Yipee! All of the teachers are gone.

Ohhh! No more teachers!
No more school!
No more lessons!
Ain't it cool?
Ain't it cool?
Ain't it cool?
Ain't it cool?

Martyn James Pullan (11)
Vermuyden School

CAN'T STOP THINKING ABOUT YOU

Roses are red
Violets are blue
You make me happy when I look at you.
With your sweet brown eyes
And your hair blowing in the wind
I can't stop thinking about you.

I can't stop looking at you
Your eyes are like sapphires
Your lips so smooth
And I
Can't stop thinking about you.

The way you walk and
The way you talk
Sends shivers to my soul.
But I can't
Stop thinking about you.

Marc Holbrough (14)
Vermuyden School

OUR LOVE

O ur love will last forever until the end of time
U nderneath the stars we sit twinkling upon high
R eaching out to hold you tight never letting you go

L over surrounds us keeping us safe and warm
O nly death could keep us from each other's everlasting love
V oices pray we will stay ever close together
E ach day my heart will grow for your evergrowing love.

Laura Huscroft (13)
Vermuyden School

NIGHT . . . !

Thinking as I lay in bed,
I get this strange thought in my head.
The sun doesn't shine
The birds don't sing
Isn't darkness a funny thing?

To think the world is asleep tonight,
To be alone gives me a fright.
I look up and look around
There's no light and no sound.

To be asleep in my bed,
Waiting for the morning again.
Everybody's asleep tonight
Can't wake them up
Or you'll give them a fright.

Night is here, go away,
Stop chasing me
Oh go away!

Jonathan Binnington (11)
Vermuyden School

LET ME BE YOURS

Let me be your perfume
Breathing in your smells.
Let me be your boy
I will never let you down.
If you like your water hot
I will be your waterspout.
Let me be yours.

Kirk Sweeting (13)
Vermuyden School

I Did Everything You Didn't Want Me To

I flirted with the other girls
I thought you would finish with me
but you didn't.

I did not come and see you
I thought you would finish with me
but you didn't.

I did everything you didn't want me to
I thought you would finish with me
but you didn't.

Now I realise that you're my everlasting love.

Andrew Harrison (13)
Vermuyden School

Sunrise

The sun rising in the east
slowly moving across the sky
through the day.
The sun slowly going over
everything and everyone.
Slowly going through the day
passing every cloud it reaches
slowly moving to the west.
For when the night falls
the sun slowly goes down.
Sparkling on the river
until the sun has gone in
and the moon takes its place.

Katherine Topping (13)
Vermuyden School

LOVERS

Love, love, love is the way we walk
down the romantic way.
Love, love, love is the time
to send you a Valentine.
Love, love, love is the treasure
for you and me to run away together.

Lauren Lyth (13)
Vermuyden School

MUSHY PEAS

I like mushy peas they are Yum! Yum!
I like them with curry or sometimes chips will do.
Buy them in a tin or pick them from a pod
any peas are tasty so if you don't like 'em your mad!
Mushy, mushy peas, Yum! Yum!
I had a bowl last night.
They gave me a fright and I knocked them all over.

Christopher Lewis (11)
Vermuyden School

NIGHT IS . . .

N ight is the scariest thing in the world.
I think that giants will get me while I'm sleeping.
G hosts will come into your room and scare you off.
H ate the dark because I'm scared.
T arantulas once came into every room in a village.

I hate spiders climbing on the wall before I go to sleep
S nakes once came into our garden.

Hiader Razak (12)
Vermuyden School

EXAMS

Waiting to go into the torture chamber
How will I do, will I pass or will I be split in two?
We stand in line, silent and scared
Ready to march into the hall of death.
Sitting at my desk having questions thrown at me
Like, what is the reciprocal of the factor squared of 89.3?
Oh my god! What are they doing to me?

Three weeks later the letter comes through
It slides through the box and lands on the mat.
Then the question comes back into my head
Will I pass or will I be dead?
Then someone said 'Well how did you do?'
I said I got A+ and A/B too.

Natalie Newham (13)
Vermuyden School

SPIDERS

Spiders, hairy, scary spiders
long legs, short legs
black legs, striped legs
round or squared.
Either way
I'm still scared.
They come into your bedroom.
They come into the bath.
They come into your bed at night
and give you half a fright.

Claire Hanlon (14)
Vermuyden School

ALONE

Now Mum's gone
no one's left
just me and the cat

    all alone

I think I'll go and watch

    TV now.

Sounds like someone's here
Don't be stupid
it's probably just the cat.
But
No it won't be any murderer
not in this house.
Just in case
go get the hammer.
There you go again
being stupid.
Better to be safe than sorry.
True!

Alright then
go get the hammer.

Something's moving upstairs
silly me just Gizmo.

I'll just go in the living room
and watch some telly.
No need to worry
Mum'll be back
soon.

I hope!

Martin Singh (13)
Vermuyden School

I WANT YOU BACK

We had an argument
I didn't want to know,
but now you've gone . . .
I want you back.

We had a life together
I didn't miss one moment,
but now you've gone
I want you back.

We had magic in our memories
I didn't miss one photo,
but now you've gone
I want you back.

We had sunshine going around with us
I didn't miss one shine,
but now you've gone
I want you back.

We had love in our hands
I didn't miss one spark,
and now your here
I've got you back.

Jessica Sharp (13)
Vermuyden School

NIGHT IS . . .

It is dark
the lights are out
the cats are crying.
The sounds of the rattling
and creaking of the monsters
coming to get me.

The bats flying
past my bedroom window
scratching it as they go.
The shadows making
ghostly shapes
moving round my room.
Bark. Ahhhrrr.
The dogs turn into wolves.
As the night goes on
I don't think I will
ever go to
     S
      l
       e
       e
        p.

Holly Youngman (11)
Vermuyden School

BULLY NIGHT

Night, night, bully night,
You always seem to gimme a fright.

The noises you make,
The images you create,
You usually keep me awake.

Night, night, bully night,
You always seem to gimme a fright.

Headlights on,
Bogeymen upon,
I shout me mam but she has gone.

Night, night, bully night.

Nicky Kerr (11)
Vermuyden School

HOMEWORK

Homework sits on top of Sunday, squashing Sunday flat.
Homework has the smell of Monday, homework's very flat.
Heavy books and piles of paper, answers I don't know.
Sunday evenings almost finished, now I'm going to go.
Do my homework in the kitchen, maybe just a snack,
Then I'll sit right down and start as soon as I run back,
For some chocolate sandwich cookies, then I'll really do
All that homework in a minute, first I'll see what new,
Shows they've got on television in the living room,
Everybody's laughing there, but misery and gloom.
But a full refrigerator are where I am at.
I'll just have another sandwich. Homework's very fat.

Matthew Johnson (15)
Vermuyden School

THE OLD ROCKING HORSE
(Dedicated to Laura Hailstone)

The old rocking horse,
Stands all alone in the nursery.
Saddle worn and reins broken,
Hair matted and falling out.
Yet still the children's friend.

Rocker broken,
Chipped wood and paint.
Grey dusty colours,
That were once gleaming white.
Broken down and destined for a tip.
Unclean but loved.
The old rocking horse.

Standing high and long,
Large enough to be sat upon.
Once it stood
King of the nursery.
Now it looks the oldest
And least loved toy.
Alas, untrue.
Being the children's favourite.

Polished and washed so new,
Now the once-known king of the nursery,
Returns to its place of honour.
Still the children's favourite toy,
Loved still more.
The old rocking horse.

Samantha Woolley (12)
Vermuyden School

MYSELF

My mum always tells me what I was like.
And she says.
When you were born you weren't half cute.
Twelve weeks old already she'd say and you were a right
little munchkin.
Your first birthday arrived and you had a fab time.
A tea party I think?
You wore a frilly white dress.
With your hair in bunches.
You grew up fast she'd say.
You started school with a frown on your face.
But you went through the years quite quickly I'd say.
You left school at the age of sixteen and went to college to fulfil
your dreams.
When you left college you met this bloke.
And got married and settled down with five kids.

Samantha Pullan (12)
Vermuyden School

SUNSET

The bright sunshine begins to fade.
The sky is all shades of pink and orange.
The night sky is coming near.
All the clouds start to disappear
into the dark blue sky.
The sun getting lower, the sky getting darker.
All the stars start to appear and the
sun has gone.

Sally Rankin (13)
Vermuyden School

A Yorkshire Dialect Poem

I were workin' dawn a lane one day
Looking at the grawnd.
I bumped into the wall.
I had a nasty bump but never mind.
Ma mates were making fun of me.
I told um to shut up.
I carried on walking.
I heard ma mam shouting.
I ran for ma life.
I thought she wa fighting.
When I got there she was arguing.
So I told her to come here.
But she told me to bog off.
I walked back dawn the lane again
And ma head were bright red.

Patricia Thompson (11)
Vermuyden School

Nitty Nan

My best nan had a problem with nits.
She tired to get rid of them
but they still bit her head to bits.
She lost all her hair and found it was bare.
They bit all her head away
and her body started to rot away.
To my surprise my mum told me
my best nan had died.
Then I found out my best nan
had a bad problem with nits.

Benjamin Hattersley (11)
Vermuyden School

NIGHT IS

Night is dark, scary, frightening and quiet.
You can hear your heart beating out loud.
You think somebody's watching.
You can hear the wind howling,
And every little noise something makes.

Melissa Nicholls (11)
Vermuyden School

NOISES OF THE NIGHT

N oises, what are they?
I   rritating noises.
G oing out in the dark, not knowing what's round
     the next corner.
H orrifying shadows.
T errified of what could be behind the door?

Damon Farmery (11)
Vermuyden School

AT NIGHT-TIME

Night is very frightening especially in the dark,
It is also very spooky especially in the park.

Night is very scary especially
When you're on your own
But when you have a light
You don't feel scared at all.

Emma Whiteley (12)
Vermuyden School

MY MAM

My mam she loves me to shreds
She feeds me on cabbage and potatoes
'They're good for you my dear,'
'Come and give us a cuddle.
Go wash your hair,
And don't forget . . . ' *n*
'Mam your starting to
get on my nerves.'
'Now dear it's time for bed'
'Oh mum it's only half-past eight!'
'Go and brush your teeth love and straight to bed'
I don't want you tired in the morning for school
Now up you go, and don't forget . . . '
'Mum I know.'

Leah Maw (12)
Vermuyden School

GOODBYE!

The time had come to say goodbye,
A shed of tears, a lonely cry.
You held my hand and kissed my cheek,
I couldn't bring myself to speak.

We shared good times, we shared bad,
Just remember the fun we had.
Always there by my side,
Taking life, stride by stride.

The time had come to say goodbye,
To leave our sorrows way behind.

Kirsty Morritt (14)
Vermuyden School

IT'S HIM . . .

Look at them, pathetic,
stupid.
He's just trying to get me jealous.
Or is he?

She's got blonde hair
and blue eyes.
What has she got that I haven't?

Maybe it's her flirting.
Yea.
Yea that's probably it.

No.
No, his arm around her,
her of all people.
It's him,
him, he's the flirt.

Kelly Noon (13)
Vermuyden School

NIGHT IS . . .

N ight is the time to sleep,
   Though others say it's time for a scare.
I n your room scared stiff,
G etting more worried about what will happen,
H earing the wind howling,
T he time to turn the lights out is *now!*

I s this the end, or are you safe?
S o now you have the answer.

Andrew Beecham (11
Vermuyden School

A Scottish Dialect Poem

'Oh, I canny get to sleep,
I know uh's playing those ear-piercin' bag pipes'
'I canny take it Mammy,'
'Oh I know love.'

Rubbin' me itchy eyelids I gad up,
huggin' me teddy bear, ran to me mam's room,
'I wanna drink er wader,
Mam what's that noise Mam?

'Oh just go back to bedroom love,'
'But Mammy I wanna drink er wader.'
eie silence at last!

Alice Wilkinson (11)
Vermuyden School

Night Is . . .

It's 12 o'clock and I'm in bed
It's time to awake the living dead.
A headless horse with a horrible corpse
Coming in the light, comes a silver knight.
Bats and black cats I do not like.
Slowly I get out of bed,
Then there goes the living dead.
I turn my light on, no one's there,
All my room is totally bare.

Matthew Sacré (11)
Vermuyden School

NIGHT

Is when the world is dark, dull and bare,
When I can see nothing there.
Looking outside fluttering by,
Black bats swooping across the sky.
It's chilly out here all alone,
I really do want to go home.
It's spooky out here all alone,
In the cold night air.
A monster, vampire or a grizzly bear.
Gazing up at little sparkly dots,
A moon, clouds lots and lots.
The wind is howling and the ghosts are prowling,
I really do want to run and run home.

Lisa Barry (12)
Vermuyden School

ALL THROUGH THE NIGHT

Night-time's very strange.
In my bed I shiver with fear.
Going up to my bedroom and jumping into bed.
Having lots of spooky dreams going around my head.
Trying not to go to sleep.
Time to go to sleep, sleep said mum
I am not tired.
My eyes start to close tight.
Every dream is different.

Laura Spence (11)
Vermuyden School

A YORKSHIRE DIALECT

It was a dark, dark night
All the lights switched off
Heard a bang, the security light came on.
The washing machine rumbling
Help! Everything's so quiet.
Hearing people talking outside my house.
Are they planning a robbery
Or is it just my mind?
Walking in Mum's bedroom
Saying 'I can't sleep'
I'm trying to get to sleep.

Help! Why is everything
So dark at night?

Abbie Victoria Wood (11)
Vermuyden School

NIGHT IS . . .

Night is the time I dread the most
I am really scared I'll see a ghost.
What's in the wardrobe?
What's under the bed?
It is a goblin without any legs?
I dare not look.
I'll have to suffer
I think I'll just stay under the cover.

Katie Nicholls (11)
Vermuyden School

A YORKSHIRE DIALECT

Awsome someone's comin'
Nah it ain't, it can't be,
Come on pucker up your lips
and give her a big smacker.
Hurry up man get it over and done with
I need the bog
Quick peg it! Cops are comin'
down ere phew! I think we've lost um.
Com'on get out your fags, I need one
Wow some chicks are comin'
Do you think all have a chance wi one?
Yerr right and pigs can fly.

Stacey Woffenden (11)
Vermuyden School

NIGHT IS

Night has no sight
street lamps are on
Light is shining on my bed
'What is that light on my bed,
on my bed,' I said
'Mummy, Mummy there's a light
on my bed, a light on my bed,'
I said, I said.
My mummy said, my mummy said
'It is the light of the night,'
she said, she said.

Thomas M Anderson (11)
Vermuyden School

Burp!

Burp, burp, burp.
Belch, belch, belch.
Is that all little Billy does?
Burp, burp, burp.
Belch, belch, belch.
What a weird day for little Billy Fuzz.
He starts of with a burp
Then it turns into a belch,
What a weird day for little Billy Fuzz.
When he has cabbage
All you hear is burp, burp, burp,
Belch, belch, belch.
What a weird day for little Billy Fuzz.

Robert Charlesworth (11)
Vermuyden School

I Can't Believe She's Gone

I still can't believe she's gone
She was only a baby, not even one
She had a cute, small, round face
Now she's gone, not a trace
I try to think, think of ways
But it's been too long, too many days
She's always there in my mind
I always think but I can't find
My memories, it's been too long
I still can't believe she's gone.

Sarah Earl (13)
Vermuyden School

NIGHT IS . . .
SECRET FEARS

I heard footsteps creeping up the stairs,
I'm scared just wanting to hide
under the covers, not daring to move.
I heard a voice, I started screaming.
My mam says, 'What's the matter?'
I told her what was wrong.
My mum said, 'You stupid wee lassy,
It's only your wee brother.'
I said 'Why am I scared?'
It's only my brother, I'm 12 years old.
What can be the matter?

Beth Kinder (11)
Vermuyden School

NIGHT IS . . .

Night is dark, dark as can be
I get scared in case someone jumps on me.
The stars are out, the sky is bright
Quick someone put on a light.
The sun is up a new day is dawning
I'm so pleased that it is *morning!*

Daniel Neil Lumley (11)
Vermuyden School

AEROPLANE

And the doors began
to shut
and the lights went on
and the pilot said
'Please fasten your belt.'
Onto the runway we went
and the hostess
came out.
'You will find your
life-jacket under your seat'
they said.
Then
all engines
go.
Forced back in our
seats.
'Happy flight'
the pilot said
as we were
forced back
like a tonne
of bricks
against our
chest
on our maiden
voyage.

Thoma JJ McGoun (13)
Vermuyden School